# Collins

# QUIZ NIGHT 2

HarperCollins Publishers
Westerhill Road
Bishopbriggs
Glasgow
G64 2QT

First Edition 2013

Reprint 10 9 8 7 6 5 4 3 2 1 0

© HarperCollins Publishers 2013

ISBN 978-0-00-752563-8

Collins® is a registered trademark of
HarperCollins Publishers Limited

www.collinsdictionary.com

A catalogue record for this book is
available from the British Library

Typeset by Davidson Publishing
Solutions, Glasgow

Printed in Great Britain by Clays Ltd,
St Ives plc

## Acknowledgements

AUTHOR
Chris Bradshaw

EDITOR
Ian Brookes

FOR THE PUBLISHER
Gerry Breslin
Lucy Cooper
Kerry Ferguson
Evelyn Sword

# Introduction

What is it that is so appealing about quizzes? What gives us so much satisfaction in recalling an obscure fact we once learned in primary school? It's hard to say. All we can say, however, is that no matter what age you are it is almost impossible to drag yourself away from a quiz once the first question has been asked.

The etymology (that's 'word history' to you and me) of quiz is, ironically, unknown. It arrived mysteriously into the English language in the 18th century and was first used to mean an odd or eccentric person. In the 19th century the meaning that we are familiar with became common and people have been taking part in quizzes ever since. Types of quiz vary enormously: from highbrow quizzes where students attempt to uphold the honour of their university by answering questions ranging from particle physics to popes, through to high-stakes quizzes where one wrong answer can cost an unlucky contestant three quarters of a million pounds.

Whether you are playing for a prize or just for fun, *Collins Quiz Night 2* is here to satisfy your quizzing needs. It's the ideal book to have with you if you're sitting on a delayed train, waiting in a doctor's surgery, or huddled in a caravan praying for the rain to stop. Or, instead of watching a quiz on TV, why not have your own quiz night with family or friends?

**The quizzes**
Half of the quizzes are themed. All the classics are covered: movie quizzes, animal quizzes, written word, sport, soap opera, and history quizzes. Science and technology are covered and so is astronomy and space. There's also food and drink, countries, the human body, and there's even some anagrams. Everything you could want really. The other half of the quizzes are pot luck rounds, because you can never have enough of these.

The quizzes are grouped together according to how tricky they are. First come the easy ones, then medium and finally the difficult quizzes.

## Easy
The easy questions should not have you racking your brains for very long. If they do, you need to wonder if you have enough brains to rack in the first place. A few of them are trickier than others and might even be labelled as 'challenging' by some. These have been included to add some extra and unexpected excitement.

## Medium
These are the essence of a great quiz. To the quiz connoisseur they'll be a delightful starter before the main course of the difficult questions. To the rest of us they'll be a feast of mind-bogglers, brain-teasers, and head-scratchers.

## Difficult
The clue is in the name. These questions are difficult. They're taxing, demanding, tough, and tricky. Anyone who answers all these questions is either a genius or cheating. You might not want to throw too many of this level into your quiz, but they are great for spicing things up or as tie-breaker questions.

## The answers
The answers to each quiz are printed at the end of the following quiz. For example, the answers to Quiz 1-Pot Luck appear at the bottom of Quiz 2-Art. The exception to this rule is the last quiz in every level. The answers to these quizzes appear at the end of the very first quiz in the level.

## Running a quiz

*Collins Quiz Night 2* is only half-finished. (Wait! Don't demand a refund yet, read on!) People don't go to the theatre to sit and read a script. Likewise, the quizzes in this book need someone to read them out. That's you.

If you're just quizzing your family during a car journey, or your mates of an afternoon, then there's probably no need to put in lots of preparation. If you're planning on using this book to run a more organized and formal quiz however, there are a few things you need to get right before you start:

❖ Rehearse: don't just pick this book up and read out the questions cold. Go through all the quizzes you're going to use by yourself beforehand. Note down all the questions (notes look better in a quiz environment than reading from a book) and answers. Although every effort has been made to ensure that all the answers in *Collins Quiz Night 2* are correct, despite our best endeavours, mistakes may still appear. If you see an answer you are not sure is right, or if you think there is more than one possible answer, then check.

❖ Paper and writing implements: do yourself a favour and prepare enough sheets of paper for everyone to write on. The aim of the game here is to stop the mad impulse certain people feel to 'help'. They will spend ten minutes running around looking for 'scrap' paper, probably ripping up your latest novel in the process. The same problem applies to pens. Ideally, have enough for everyone. Remember, though, that over half of them will be lost forever once you've given them out.

❖ Prizes: everyone likes a prize. No matter how small, it's best to have one on offer.

Good luck! We hope you enjoy *Collins Quiz Night 2*.

# Contents

## Easy Quizzes

# Medium Quizzes

# Difficult Quizzes

# EASY QUIZZES

# Quiz 1: Pot Luck

1. According to the proverb, what makes the heart grow fonder?

2. Who in 2012 became the first British cyclist to win the Tour de France?

3. Who was re-elected as Mayor of London in 2012?

4. Nurses Jenny Lee and Chummy Brown and Dr Patrick Turner are characters in which BBC medical drama?

5. White Hart Lane is the home ground of which Premier League football club?

6. At a hospital, what do the initials A & E stand for?

7. Whom did Barack Obama succeed as President of the USA?

8. Which word, which has become popular during the economic downturn, means a holiday spent at home rather than going abroad?

9. What is the only US state that begins with the letter D?

10. What do the initials VAT stand for?

11. Gorgonzola cheese originates from which country?

12. Which TV talent show is sometimes known as 'BGT'?

13. What is the name given to the interest rate set by the Bank of England at which it will lend to other financial institutions?

14. Which long-serving EastEnders character is played by Adam Woodyatt?

15. Someone who disapproves of building near their home is said to be a 'nimby'. What does the acronym 'nimby' stand for?

16. Which word connects the early leader of a long-distance race and an electronic device to correct the functions of the heart?

17. Who is the only judge to have appeared on every season of TV show 'The X Factor'?

18. Who in March 2013 became the first South American to become pope?

19. What is the American equivalent of the UK emergency number 999?
    a) 000
    b) 119
    c) 911

20. 'The Caped Crusader' is the nickname of which superhero?
    a) Batman
    b) Spider Man
    c) Superman

## Answers to Quiz 66: Name the Year

| | | | |
|---|---|---|---|
| 1. | 1966 | 11. | 1973 |
| 2. | 1918 | 12. | 1989 |
| 3. | 2010 | 13. | 1215 |
| 4. | 1908 | 14. | 2007 |
| 5. | 1969 | 15. | 1982 |
| 6. | 2009 | 16. | 2011 |
| 7. | 1997 | 17. | 1967 |
| 8. | 2001 | 18. | 1819 |
| 9. | 1999 | 19. | 1936 |
| 10. | 1967 | 20. | 1993 |

# Quiz 2: Art

1. What implements, used by painters, can be flats, brights, rounds, longs, or filberts?

2. What name is given to an artwork made up of a combination of pieces of cloth, paper, or other found objects?

3. In which city will you find the Musée d'Orsay and the Louvre?

4. Which word describes a sculpture of the upper part of the human body?

5. 'A Bigger Splash', 'Mr and Mrs Clark and Percy', and 'Two Boys in the Pool, Hollywood' are works by which Yorkshire-born artist?

6. Which Renaissance master painted 'The Last Supper'?

7. Roy Lichtenstein is commonly associated with which art movement?

8. The Acropolis Museum is in which European city?

9. What nationality was the painter Matisse?

10. Which British painter, who died in 1992, shared his name with an Elizabethan philosopher and statesman?

11. Which cross-dressing potter won the Turner Prize in 2003?

12. Which Turner-Prize-winning British artist has also won the Palme d'Or at the Cannes Film Festival?

13. What is the name of the oven used to fire ceramics?

14. Which British gallery is situated at the former Bankside Power Station?

15. 'The Singing Butler', 'Dance Me to the End of Love', and 'Suddenly One Summer' are works by which popular contemporary Scottish artist?

16. Which French phrase describes artists who use new ideas and techniques in an innovative or experimental way?

17. 'Les Demoiselles d'Avignon' and 'Guernica' are two of the most famous works by which Spanish painter?

18. Who painted the 1889 work 'Self Portrait with Bandaged Ear'?

19. A painting that is achromatic lacks what?
    a) colour
    b) curved lines
    c) straight lines

20. Anthony Gormley is an award-winning artist in which field?
    a) painting
    b) photography
    c) sculpture

## Answers to Quiz 1: Pot Luck

1. Absence
2. Bradley Wiggins
3. Boris Johnson
4. Call the Midwife
5. Tottenham Hotspur
6. Accident and Emergency
7. George W Bush
8. Staycation
9. Delaware
10. Value Added Tax
11. Italy
12. Britain's Got Talent
13. Base rate
14. Ian Beale
15. Not in my back yard
16. Pacemaker
17. Louis Walsh
18. Francis I (Jorge Mario Bergoglio)
19. 911
20. Batman

# **Quiz 3:** Pot Luck

1.  Who played villain Raoul Silva in the 2012 film 'Skyfall'?

2.  The giant statue of Christ the Redeemer overlooks which South American city?

3.  Who is the host of TV game show 'The Chase'?

4.  What are Bonhams, Christie's, and Sotheby's?

5.  'The Power' is the nickname of which darts world champion?

6.  Which national radio station broadcasts on 909 and 693AM?

7.  Helen Worth plays which character in 'Coronation Street'?

8.  The French call it 'la Manche', but what is it known as in English?

9.  Who was the first US President to be born in the state of Hawaii?

10. Andy Warhol and Richard Hamilton are associated with which 20th-century art movement?

11. Which radio drama is set in the village of Ambridge?

12. Which city hosted the first modern Olympic Games?

13. Which British actor plays Brodie in the American television drama 'Homeland'?

14. Who left 'Strictly Come Dancing' to join the judging panel at 'Britain's Got Talent' in 2012?

15. Will McKenzie, Simon Cooper, Jay Cartwright, and Neil Sutherland are the main characters in which British comedy?

16. What connects the sidekick of fictional sleuth Hercule Poirot and a famous 11th-century battle?

17. TV comedy 'The Big Bang Theory' is set in which US state?

18. Ian Brown, John Squire, Gary Mountfield, and Alan Wren are members of which band, which reformed in 2012?

19. Which animal is used to describe an older lady with a liking for younger men?
    a) cougar
    b) panther
    c) puma

20. The Ashmolean Museum is in which English city?
    a) Oxford
    b) Cambridge
    c) Hull

EASY

## Answers to Quiz 2: Art

1. Brushes
2. Collage
3. Paris
4. Bust
5. David Hockney
6. Leonardo da Vinci
7. Pop Art
8. Athens
9. French
10. Francis Bacon
11. Grayson Perry
12. Steve McQueen
13. Kiln
14. Tate Modern
15. Jack Vettriano
16. Avant-garde
17. Pablo Picasso
18. Vincent van Gogh
19. Colour
20. Sculpture

# Quiz 4: England

1. Which two colours make the up the flag of England?

2. What is the national animal of England?

3. Who is the patron saint of England?

4. A Novocastrian is a person from which English city?

5. What is the most southerly county of England?

6. Which English sporting event traditionally takes place every year in the last week of June and the first week of July?

7. The film 'The Full Monty' was largely set in which English city?

8. Which Roman fortification in northern England stretches from Wallsend to Bowness?

9. The Avebury stone circles are in which English county?

10. On which day of the year is St George's Day celebrated?

11. London Zoo lies in which park?

12. What is England's second largest city by population?

13. What are Wormwood Scrubs, Pentonville, and Holloway?

14. The Goose Fair is held each year in which Midlands city?

15. Which major sporting event takes place each year at the Crucible Theatre in Sheffield?

16. In which English city will you find the sporting venues Trent Bridge, the City Ground, and Meadow Lane?

17. Which English city is further north – Birmingham or Norwich?

18. William Shakespeare was born on, and died on, which date?

19. The White Rose is the emblem of which English county?
    a) Lancashire
    b) Warwickshire
    c) Yorkshire

20. The Clifton Suspension Bridge spans which river?
    a) Avon
    b) Severn
    c) Thames

EASY

## Answers to Quiz 3: Pot Luck

1. Javier Bardem
2. Rio de Janeiro
3. Bradley Walsh
4. Auction houses
5. Phil Taylor
6. BBC Radio 5 Live
7. Gail Platt
8. The English Channel
9. Barack Obama
10. Pop Art
11. The Archers
12. Athens
13. Damian Lewis
14. Alesha Dixon
15. The Inbetweeners
16. Hastings
17. California
18. The Stone Roses
19. Cougar
20. Oxford

# Quiz 5: Pot Luck

1. According to the proverb, don't count your chickens until they are what?

2. Mario, Arg, Kurt, and Kirk regularly appear in which reality TV show?

3. In British politics, what do the initials UKIP stand for?

4. Shaivism, Vaishnavism, and Ðrauta are branches of which religion?

5. The United Kingdom shares a land border with which country?

6. Chiropody is a branch of medicine that deals with which part of the body?

7. Tim Wonnacott succeeded David Dickinson as the host of which daytime TV show?

8. What are the five US states that end with the letter S?

9. Greg Rutherford won gold at the 2012 Olympic Games in which athletics event?

10. What type of animal was part of the winning act on the 2012 series of 'Britain's Got Talent'?

11. Which London landmark is the tallest building in Western Europe?

12. What is the name of the symbol stamped on precious metals to show they have been tested at an Assay Office?

13. What is the value of the only bi-colour coin in Britain?

14. In finance, what do the initials AER stand for?

15. Which ancient Greek philosopher was condemned to die by drinking hemlock?

16. Which term describes a house that is bought solely to rent out rather than live in?

17. Former footballer Alan Brazil hosts the breakfast show on which national radio station?

18. Which swimmer became the most decorated Olympian in history after winning his 19th medal at the 2012 games?

19. In which decade did the National Health Service come into being?
    a) 1930s
    b) 1940s
    c) 1950s

20. Which of the following animals does not give its name to a year in the Chinese calendar?
    a) dog
    b) pig
    c) hamster

## Answers to Quiz 4: England

1. White and red
2. Lion
3. St George
4. Newcastle upon Tyne
5. Cornwall
6. Wimbledon
7. Sheffield
8. Hadrian's Wall
9. Wiltshire
10. 23rd April
11. Regent's Park
12. Birmingham
13. London prisons
14. Nottingham
15. The World Snooker Championships
16. Nottingham
17. Norwich
18. 23rd April
19. Yorkshire
20. Avon

# Quiz 6: Food and Drink

EASY

1. Bloomer, naan, and focaccia are varieties of what type of food?

2. Dim sum is a dish from the cuisine of which country?

3. On which day of the week is a roast beef dinner traditionally served in Britain?

4. What name is given to small cubes of bread served in soup?

5. Chai, oolong, and Lapsang Souchong are varieties of what type of drink?

6. Pesto is made using the leaves of which herb?

7. What is the main ingredient in the Indian dish biryani?

8. At what time of the year would you eat a cake called a stollen?

9. Which award-winning chef runs a restaurant in Bray called The Fat Duck?

10. Paneer, halloumi, and feta are types of what?

11. A dish served 'au gratin' is usually covered with what?

12. The Melton Mowbray pork pie is named after a town in which Midlands county?

13. Which Yorkshire-born chef is the host of the BBC cooking show 'Saturday Kitchen'?

14. What colour is the highly alcoholic drink absinthe?

15. Strawberries and cream are traditionally served at which annual sporting event?

16. What is the main ingredient of the alcoholic drink perry?

17. What are Si King and Dave Myers better known as?

18. Manchego cheese comes from which country?

19. A wok is a pan traditionally used in what type of cooking?
    a) Indian
    b) Italian
    c) Chinese

20. Shortbread is associated with which part of Britain?
    a) England
    b) Scotland
    c) Wales

EASY

## Answers to Quiz 5: Pot Luck

1. Hatched
2. The Only Way Is Essex
3. United Kingdom Independence Party
4. Hinduism
5. The Republic of Ireland
6. Feet
7. Bargain Hunt
8. Arkansas, Illinois, Kansas, Massachusetts, and Texas
9. Long jump
10. Dog
11. The Shard
12. Hallmark
13. £2
14. Annual Equivalent Rate
15. Socrates
16. Buy-to-let
17. TalkSport
18. Michael Phelps
19. 1940s
20. Hamster

# Quiz 7: Pot Luck

EASY

1. Complete the proverb: 'a problem shared is a problem ...'

2. Niall Horan, Zayn Malik, Liam Payne, Harry Styles, and Louis Tomlinson are members of which band?

3. Tiananmen Square is in which Asian capital city?

4. What is the name of the character played by Patsy Palmer in BBC soap 'EastEnders'?

5. Charles de Gaulle Airport serves which European city?

6. What sort of rating is used to assess the worthiness of a potential borrower?

7. Which country has won the most medals in the history of the Olympic Games?

8. Jazz musician Kenny Ball, who died in 2013, was associated with which musical instrument?

9. What is the highest mountain in England?

10. Which word describes a person who exposes wrongdoing within an organization in the hope of stopping it?

11. Citizens from which non-British or Commonwealth country are allowed to vote in UK elections?

12. What gas has the atomic number 7 and the chemical symbol N?

13. 'Naranja' is the Spanish word for which fruit?

14. Heath Ledger played which villain in 'Batman: The Dark Knight'?

15. What do the initials RSPCA stand for?

16. What is the official residence of the President of Russia?

17. What item of clothing is also used to describe a boring person with a tedious hobby?

18. Which political leader said, 'An eye for an eye only ends up making the whole world blind'?

19. What sort of shop did Macklemore and Ryan Lewis sing about on their 2013 number one hit?
    a) Charity Shop
    b) Pet Shop
    c) Thrift Shop

20. Which national radio station broadcasts on 88 to 91 FM?
    a) BBC Radio 1
    b) BBC Radio 2
    c) BBC Radio 3

## Answers to Quiz 6: Food and Drink

1. Bread
2. China
3. Sunday
4. Croutons
5. Tea
6. Basil
7. Rice
8. Christmas
9. Heston Blumenthal
10. Cheese
11. Breadcrumbs
12. Leicestershire
13. James Martin
14. Green
15. Wimbledon
16. Pears
17. The Hairy Bikers
18. Spain
19. Chinese
20. Scotland

# Quiz 8: Films

1. What film, set amidst the Iran hostage crisis, won the Oscar for Best Picture in 2013?

2. Which British actor's films include 'Layer Cake', 'Cowboys & Aliens', and 'The Girl with the Dragon Tattoo'?

3. Which British actor played Albert the butler in 'The Dark Knight Rises'?

4. Who directed the political biopic 'Lincoln'?

5. Which Cockney heavyweight played Jack Regan in the 2012 film version of 'The Sweeney'?

6. The 2008 film 'Slumdog Millionaire' is set in which country?

7. Who won the 2013 Oscar for Best Actress for her performance in 'Silver Linings Playbook'?

8. The hit comedy 'The Hangover' was largely set in which city?

9. Which British-born actor is the only man to win the Oscar for Best Actor three times?

10. What is the name of the character played by Michael J Fox in the 'Back to the Future' trilogy?

11. Which British actor played Bilbo Baggins in the 2012 film 'The Hobbit'?

12. Which film trilogy centred on the Corleone family?

13. Arnold Schwarzenegger first uttered the famous line 'I'll be back' in which film?

14. 'Zero Dark Thirty' is a film about the quest to find which person?

15. Who played Frodo in Peter Jackson's 'The Lord of the Rings' trilogy?

16. 'Frankly, my dear, I don't give a damn' is a famous line from which classic film?

17. Which female British singer sang the theme song to the James Bond film 'Skyfall'?

18. Which director's films include 'Vertigo', 'Psycho', and 'North by Northwest'?

19. Which sport features in the films 'Raging Bull', 'The Hurricane', and 'Cinderella Man'?
    a) baseball
    b) boxing
    c) football

20. Which film topped the UK box office charts in 2012?
    a) 'Taken 2'
    b) 'Skyfall'
    c) 'The Dark Knight Rises'

## Answers to Quiz 7: Pot Luck

1. Halved
2. One Direction
3. Beijing
4. Bianca Butcher
5. Paris
6. Credit rating
7. USA
8. Trumpet
9. Scafell Pike
10. Whistleblower
11. Republic of Ireland
12. Nitrogen
13. Orange
14. The Joker
15. Royal Society for the Prevention of Cruelty to Animals
16. The Kremlin
17. Anorak
18. Gandhi
19. Thrift Shop
20. BBC Radio 2

# Quiz 9: Pot Luck

EASY

1. Sunni and Shia are branches of which religion?

2. In finance, what do the initials NS&I stand for?

3. What is the name of the alternative therapy that uses gentle pressure on the hands and especially the feet?

4. What are the two US states that end in the letter D?

5. Which word describes an activity popular with children in winter and a form of verbal intimidation used by cricketers?

6. In radio, what do the initials DAB stand for?

7. Which term is used to describe the act of a reigning monarch renouncing their royal office?

8. Which city hosted the 2004 Olympic Games?

9. Who is Britain's oldest ever monarch?

10. 'I' is the sister publication of which national newspaper?

11. Which actress led a 2009 campaign for settlement rights for Gurkha soldiers who had served in the British Army?

12. Which BBC national radio network broadcasts on 90-93 FM?

13. What is 2013 in roman numerals?

14. Which word describes lying in a court case after swearing an oath to tell the truth?

15. Thom Yorke is the lead singer with which British rock band?

16. The leaf of which tree appears on the flag of Canada?

EASY

17. Which member of The Pussycat Dolls joined the judging panel of 'The X Factor' in 2012?

18. In UK politics, what do the initials DUP stand for?

19. Which actor played the title character in the 2012 film 'Django Unchained'?
a) Don Cheadle
b) Jamie Foxx
c) Will Smith

20. Complete the title of a 1951 Hitchcock classic film: 'Strangers on a ...'
a) Boat
b) Plane
c) Train

## Answers to Quiz 8: Films

1. Argo
2. Daniel Craig
3. Michael Caine
4. Steven Spielberg
5. Ray Winstone
6. India
7. Jennifer Lawrence
8. Las Vegas
9. Daniel Day-Lewis
10. Marty McFly
11. Martin Freeman
12. The Godfather
13. The Terminator
14. Osama bin Laden
15. Elijah Wood
16. Gone with the Wind
17. Adele
18. Alfred Hitchcock
19. Boxing
20. Skyfall

# Quiz 10: History

1. Which English monarch had six wives?

2. Whom did David Cameron succeed as prime minister of Britain?

3. In relation to history, what do the initials BCE stand for?

4. Which famous battle is also the title of a 1974 number one hit by Abba?

5. Fidel Castro was the long-time leader of which country?

6. What battle is shown on the Bayeux Tapestry?

7. Florence Nightingale rose to prominence while serving as a nurse in which war?

8. In which year was US president John F Kennedy assassinated?

9. Fireworks were invented in which country?

10. England and which other country were involved in the 100 Years War?

11. Colonel Gaddafi was formerly the leader of which African country?

12. A Japanese attack on which Hawaiian base in 1941 brought America into World War II?

13. Who is the only US president to resign from office?

14. Napoleon Bonaparte was emperor of which country?

15. Who was the second emperor of Rome?

16. Who was assassinated by James Earl Ray in Memphis in 1968?

EASY

17. Who was the president of Egypt from 1981 until 2011?

18. Which European country was the site of a bloody civil war between 1936 and 1939?

19. Who was Britain's longest serving Labour prime minister?
    a) Clement Attlee
    b) Tony Blair
    c) Harold Wilson

20. In which year was the Act of Union between England and Scotland passed?
    a) 1607
    b) 1707
    c) 1807

## Answers to Quiz 9: Pot Luck

1. Islam
2. National Savings and Investments
3. Reflexology
4. Maryland and Rhode Island
5. Sledging
6. Digital Audio Broadcasting
7. Abdication
8. Athens
9. Queen Elizabeth II
10. The Independent
11. Joanna Lumley
12. Radio 3
13. MMXIII
14. Perjury
15. Radiohead
16. Maple
17. Nicole Scherzinger
18. Democratic Unionist Party
19. Jamie Foxx
20. Train

# Quiz 11: Pot Luck

1.  According to the proverb, what is mightier than the sword?

2.  On what date is Remembrance Day commemorated each year?

3.  Who was the first Queen of England to reign in her own right rather than through marriage to a king?

4.  What name is given to a tennis serve that isn't touched by the receiver?

5.  Which state of America has the largest population?

6.  The Ballon d'Or is awarded to the best player of the year in which sport?

7.  The Battle of Stalingrad was a bloody conflict in which war?

8.  The Knesset is the legislature of which country?

9.  Which actor played Aragorn in Peter Jackson's 'The Lord of the Rings' trilogy?

10. Which British actor and comedian is married to Dutch model Lara Stone?

11. The headquarters of the European Commission are in which city?

12. The spirit tequila takes its name from a town in which country?

13. Shayne Ward is a former winner of which reality TV show?

14. Bella Swan and Edward Cullen are the main characters in which vampire-inspired book and film series?

15. In relation to drinks, what do the initials ABV stand for?

16.  A saltire argent in a field azure describes the flag of which part of Britain?

17.  Which former Conservative politician hosts the TV series 'Great British Railway Journeys'?

18.  Parti Québécois is a political movement in which country?

19.  Which of the following is the title of a 2008 film starring Colin Farrell?
     a) In Amsterdam
     b) In Bruges
     c) In Brussels

20.  Which of the following animals does not give its name to a year in the Chinese calendar?
     a) lion
     b) rooster
     c) tiger

## Answers to Quiz 10: History

| | |
|---|---|
| 1. Henry VIII | 11. Libya |
| 2. Gordon Brown | 12. Pearl Harbor |
| 3. Before Common Era | 13. Richard Nixon |
| 4. Waterloo | 14. France |
| 5. Cuba | 15. Tiberius |
| 6. The Battle of Hastings | 16. Martin Luther King |
| 7. Crimean War | 17. Hosni Mubarak |
| 8. 1963 | 18. Spain |
| 9. China | 19. Tony Blair |
| 10. France | 20. 1707 |

# Quiz 12: Books

1. Which author created the fictional detectives Miss Marple and Hercule Poirot?

2. Which pukka TV chef wrote the bestseller '15 Minute Meals'?

3. Elizabeth Bennet and Mr Darcy are the main characters in which novel by Jane Austen?

4. 'Still Standing: The Savage Years' is the title of which comedian, actor, and broadcaster's 2012 autobiography?

5. Which author wrote 'The Hobbit' and 'The Lord of the Rings'?

6. What is the first name of Henning Mankell's fictional detective Wallander?

7. Which seventies heartthrob turned 'EastEnders' star's autobiography is called 'Over The Moon'?

8. The musical 'Les Miserables' is based on a novel by which French author?

9. 'Of Mice and Men' is by which Depression-era American author?

10. Which hirsute pair of TV chefs wrote the best-selling cookery book, 'How to Love Food and Lose Weight'?

11. With which sport would you associate an almanack known as 'Wisden'?

12. 'A Short History of Nearly Everything', 'At Home: A Short History of Private Life', and 'Notes From a Small Island' are books by which British-based American author?

13. Who created the classic comedic characters Jeeves and Wooster?

14. Atticus Finch, Boo Radley, Scout, and Jem are characters in which novel by Harper Lee?

15. 'The Clifton Chronicles' are a series of books by which politician-turned-writer?

16. 'Unseen Academicals', 'I Shall Wear Midnight', and 'Snuff' are recent additions to which series of fantasy novels by Terry Pratchett?

17. Which literary sisters were from the Yorkshire town of Haworth?

18. Miss Havisham, Pip, and Herbert Pocket are characters in which novel by Charles Dickens?

19. Complete the title of the children's book by Julia Donaldson that was made into a 2012 animated film: 'Room on the ...'
a) Broom  b) Loom  c) Mushroom

20. Complete the title of the 2006 thriller by Stieg Larsson: 'The Girl Who Played with ...'
a) Fire  b) Petrol  c) Dolls

**EASY**

## Answers to Quiz 11: Pot Luck

1. The pen
2. 11 November
3. Queen Mary I
4. Ace
5. California
6. Football
7. World War II
8. Israel
9. Viggo Mortensen
10. David Walliams
11. Brussels
12. Mexico
13. The X Factor
14. Twilight
15. Alcohol By Volume
16. Scotland
17. Michael Portillo
18. Canada
19. In Bruges
20. Lion

# Quiz 13: Pot Luck

1. Proverbially, by what should you not judge a book?

2. The 2011 release 'Up All Night' was the debut album by which best-selling band?

3. Who is the host of the TV quiz 'QI'?

4. The England rugby union team plays its home matches at which stadium?

5. A cross gules in a field argent describes the flag of which part of Britain?

6. Which actor played James Bond for the only time in 'On Her Majesty's Secret Service'?

7. In relation to finance, what do the initials ECB stand for?

8. The Gobi Desert stretches across vast swathes of which two countries?

9. In which part of the UK are there political parties known as the SDLP, DUP, and the Alliance?

10. Whom did Ed Miliband beat in the final vote to become leader of the Labour Party in 2010?

11. Which Indian city hosted the 2010 Commonwealth Games?

12. In which sport might you expect to see googlies, wrong'uns, and doosras?

13. Mount McKinley, the highest point in North America, is in which US state?

14. What spirit is the main ingredient in the liqueur Malibu?

15. In UK imperial measurements, how many pints are in a gallon?

EASY

16. According to the the proverb, 'two wrongs don't make a...'?

17. Dutch, French, and German are the official languages of which European country?

18. The Alpine ski resorts of Val d'Isere and Chamonix are in which country?

19. In which year was the Battle of Agincourt fought?
    a) 1415
    b) 1514
    c) 1541

20. Damon Albarn is the lead singer with which group?
    a) Blur
    b) Oasis
    c) Pulp

## Answers to Quiz 12: Books

1.  Agatha Christie
2.  Jamie Oliver
3.  Pride and Prejudice
4.  Paul O'Grady
5.  JRR Tolkien
6.  Kurt
7.  David Essex
8.  Victor Hugo
9.  John Steinbeck
10. The Hairy Bikers
11. Cricket
12. Bill Bryson
13. PG Wodehouse
14. To Kill a Mockingbird
15. Jeffrey Archer
16. Discworld
17. The Brontë sisters
18. Great Expectations
19. Broom
20. Fire

# Quiz 14: Money

1. How many sides does a 20p coin have?

2. Prior to its adopting the euro, what was the currency of Germany?

3. What is the name of the body that manufactures coins in the UK?

4. Which comedian was forced to apologize in 2013 after being caught using a legal loophole to avoid paying taxes?

5. What is the fewest number of coins you need to make a total of 45p?

6. Greenback is slang for which currency?

7. What is the highest value banknote produced by the Bank of England?

8. From 1968 until 2008, a Scottish thistle appeared on the tails side of which coin?

9. An image of which composer appeared on the back of the £20 note from 1999 to 2010?

10. Which broadcaster sold his MoneySavingExpert.com website for £87m in June 2012?

11. Which animal appears on the reverse of a 10p piece?

12. Which economist appears on the £20 note?

13. The ECB is based in which German city?

14. Carlos Slim Helu, the richest man in the world, is from which country?

15. A portcullis appears on the tails side of which British coin?

16. What is the currency of India?

17. In UK finance, what does the acronym ISA stand for?

18. The escudo is the former currency of which European country?

19. Which actor played the title character Billy Beane in the Oscar-nominated 2011 film 'Moneyball'?
    a) George Clooney
    b) Ewan McGregor
    c) Brad Pitt

20. Which of these countries does not have the euro as its currency?
    a) Austria
    b) Luxembourg
    c) Switzerland

## Answers to Quiz 13: Pot Luck

| | |
|---|---|
| 1. Its cover | 11. New Delhi |
| 2. One Direction | 12. Cricket |
| 3. Stephen Fry | 13. Alaska |
| 4. Twickenham | 14. White rum |
| 5. England | 15. 8 |
| 6. George Lazenby | 16. Right |
| 7. European Central Bank | 17. Belgium |
| 8. China and Mongolia | 18. France |
| 9. Northern Ireland | 19. 1415 |
| 10. His brother, David Miliband | 20. Blur |

# Quiz 15: Pot Luck

1. Whom did Barack Obama defeat to win the 2012 US presidential election?

2. Which dancer succeeded Alesha Dixon as a judge on 'Strictly Come Dancing'?

3. Which dapper Olympian won the 2012 BBC Sports Personality of the Year award?

4. In tennis, which word is used when the score is 40-all?

5. What is sodium chloride more commonly known as?

6. Who retired from international rugby in 2011 after scoring an English-record 1,179 points?

7. The island of Madagascar lies in which ocean?

8. The disease retinitis pigmentosa affects which part of the body?

9. Amy Pond was a companion of which time-travelling TV character?

10. What form of transport is associated with HS2?

11. The island of Zealand is part of which Scandinavian country?

12. What colour helmets are worn by soldiers on United Nations peacekeeping assignments?

13. Bashar al-Assad is the leader of which Arab country?

14. Which country left the Commonwealth in 1961 but rejoined in 1994?

15. The Bernabeu Stadium is the home ground of which European football club?

Answers – page 33

16. What is the only state of America that starts with the letter R?

17. What do the initials DVLA stand for?

18. Which Scottish singer won 'Britain's Got Talent' in 2011?

19. How many squares are there on a chess board?
    a) 36
    b) 64
    c) 144

20. Mark Billingham is associated with what genre of fiction?
    a) crime
    b) espionage
    c) science fiction

## Answers to Quiz 14: Money

1. Seven
2. Deutsche Mark
3. The Royal Mint
4. Jimmy Carr
5. 3
6. US dollar
7. £50
8. 5p
9. Edward Elgar
10. Martin Lewis
11. Lion
12. Adam Smith
13. Frankfurt
14. Mexico
15. 1p
16. Rupee
17. Individual Savings Account
18. Portugal
19. Brad Pitt
20. Switzerland

# Quiz 16: Pop Music

1. 'Sound of the Underground' was the debut single from which British girl group?

2. Who topped the charts for 16 weeks in 1991 with '(Everything I Do) I Do It For You'?

3. What are Irish brothers John and Edward Grimes better known as?

4. Which member of the Black Eyed Peas is a judge on TV talent show 'The Voice'?

5. Roger Daltrey is the lead singer of which British rock band?

6. 'Our Version of Events' is the debut album by which British singer?

7. 'Exile on Main Street', 'Beggars Banquet' and 'Sticky Fingers' are albums from which veteran rockers?

8. 'Definitely Maybe' was the debut album from which band?

9. Which girl group announced that it would be splitting up after its tenth anniversary tour in 2013?

10. What title is shared by a number 3 hit by Ed Sheeran in 2011 and a 1980s drama?

11. Who beat Olly Murs to win the sixth season of 'The X Factor'?

12. 'Babel' was a best-selling album in 2012 for which British band?

13. Suggs is the lead singer with which band?

14. What are the pop duo Neil Tennant and Chris Lowe more commonly known as?

15. 'Who's That Girl', 'Frozen', and 'True Blue' were number one hits for which female singer?

16. Which US hip-hop star, whose name sounds like a US state, had 2012 hits with 'Wild Ones' and 'Whistle'?

17. What do the initials MOBO stand for?

18. 'Somebody That I Used to Know' was biggest selling single in the UK in 2012. Who recorded it?

19. Complete the title of a 2012 hit for Coldplay: 'Princess of ...'
    a) China
    b) India
    c) Wales

20. Blondie topped the charts in 1979 with 'Heart of ...'?
    a) Glass
    b) Oak
    c) Stone

**EASY**

## Answers to Quiz 15: Pot Luck

1. Mitt Romney
2. Darcey Bussell
3. Bradley Wiggins
4. Deuce
5. Salt
6. Jonny Wilkinson
7. Indian Ocean
8. Eye
9. Doctor Who
10. Railways
11. Denmark
12. Light blue
13. Syria
14. South Africa
15. Real Madrid
16. Rhode Island
17. Driver and Vehicle Licensing Agency
18. Jai McDowall
19. 64
20. Crime

# Quiz 17: Pot Luck

1. Proverbially, what is only skin-deep?

2. At which stadium does the Scotland rugby union team usually play its home matches?

3. Which word describes a work of art created using small tiles?

4. Which animal features on the Royal Standard?

5. Which word describes a rock that enters Earth's atmosphere from outer space and reaches the ground?

6. Which British national newspaper is nicknamed 'The Thunderer'?

7. Ibrox Park is the home ground of which British football club?

8. Milhous was the middle name of which American president?

9. Seville and Malaga are the main cities in which region of Spain?

10. Which terrestrial channel first appeared on UK TV screens in 1982?

11. Tony Barton managed which English European Cup-winning football team?

12. Henry Blofeld, Richie Benaud, and Jonathan Agnew are commentators on which sport?

13. Roquefort cheese comes from which country?

14. What do the initials GMT stand for?

15. Who was the only British monarch of the House of Saxe-Coburg-Gotha?

16. Jovian is an adjective that relates to which planet?

17. A sarcophagus is a type of what?

18. The Museum of Modern Art and the Metropolitan Museum of Art are in which American city?

19. In which year did Margaret Thatcher become Britain's first female prime minister?
    a) 1974
    b) 1979
    c) 1983

20. Which of the following was a 2013 dance craze?
    a) Brooklyn Shake
    b) Harlem Shake
    c) Manhattan Shake

EASY

## Answers to Quiz 16: Pop Music

1. Girls Aloud
2. Bryan Adams
3. Jedward
4. Will.I.Am
5. The Who
6. Emeli Sandè
7. The Rolling Stones
8. Oasis
9. Girls Aloud
10. The A Team
11. Joe McElderry
12. Mumford and Sons
13. Madness
14. The Pet Shop Boys
15. Madonna
16. Flo Rida
17. Music Of Black Origin
18. Gotye
19. China
20. Glass

# Quiz 18: Science and Technology

EASY

1. What chemical element has the symbol O and the atomic number 8?

2. Kelvin is a unit used to measure what?

3. Which Polish astronomer suggested that the Sun and not the Earth is at the centre of the universe?

4. A lactometer is used to measure the density of which liquid?

5. Which German-born scientist said, 'Imagination is more important than knowledge'?

6. Around 73% of the Sun is made up of which element?

7. Seismology is the study of what?

8. Conduction and convection are two of the three ways that heat can be transferred. What is the third?

9. Whose Third Law of Motion states that for every action there is an equal and opposite reaction?

10. What is deoxyribonucleic acid more commonly known as?

11. What two-word phrase describes what happens when the Earth passes through the Moon's shadow?

12. What is the most common gas in the earth's atmosphere?

13. Which element has the atomic number 1 on the periodic table?

14. In the equation $E=mc^2$ what does the M stand for?

15. In which decade were compact discs released commercially for the first time?

16. The word 'taikonaut' is used to describe space travellers from which country?

17. Which astronomer and broadcaster died in December 2012 at the age of 89?

18. What is the branch of physics that deals with the motion of air?

19. Which branch of science is concerned with the study of living things and their vital processes?
    a) biology
    b) chemistry
    c) physics

20. What is the star Polaris more commonly known as?
    a) North Star
    b) South Star
    c) West Star

## Answers to Quiz 17: Pot Luck

1. Beauty
2. Murrayfield
3. Mosaic
4. Lion
5. Meteorite
6. The Times
7. Rangers
8. Richard Nixon
9. Andalusia
10. Channel 4
11. Aston Villa
12. Cricket
13. France
14. Greenwich Mean Time
15. King Edward VII
16. Jupiter
17. Coffin
18. New York
19. 1979
20. Harlem Shake

# Quiz 19: Pot Luck

1.  In which city will you find a major sporting stadium called Lansdowne Road?

2.  Who directed the 2012 film 'Django Unchained'?

3.  Who was the first president of the USA?

4.  What famous portrait is also known as 'La Gioconda'?

5.  According to the proverb, what will move mountains?

6.  Who is the only person in Britain who can drive without a licence or a registration number on their car?

7.  Portuguese is the official language of which South American country?

8.  @Pontifex is the official Twitter handle of the holder of which post?

9.  Copacabana and Ipanema are areas of which city?

10. Las Vegas is the largest city in which US state?

11. Which French actor fled his homeland in protest at high taxes and was awarded Russian citizenship?

12. At which English racecourse is the Grand National held?

13. What are the two official languages of Canada?

14. Benjamin 'Bibi' Netanyahu is a political leader in which Middle Eastern country?

15. What is the first book in the Harry Potter series?

16. Which country joined rugby's Six Nations Championship in 2000?

17. In a game of chess, the player with which colour pieces moves first – black or white?

18. What is the second largest city in Spain by population?

19. What would you do with a 'bruschetta'?
    a) drink it
    b) eat it
    c) wear it

20. What was the name of the 2012 time-travel drama starring Bruce Willis and Joseph Gordon-Levitt?
    a) Hooper
    b) Looper
    c) Snooper

## Answers to Quiz 18: Science and Technology

| | | | |
|---|---|---|---|
| 1. | Oxygen | 11. | Solar eclipse |
| 2. | Temperature | 12. | Nitrogen |
| 3. | Nicolaus Copernicus | 13. | Hydrogen |
| 4. | Milk | 14. | Mass |
| 5. | Albert Einstein | 15. | 1980s |
| 6. | Hydrogen | 16. | China |
| 7. | Earthquakes | 17. | Sir Patrick Moore |
| 8. | Radiation | 18. | Aerodynamics |
| 9. | Newton's | 19. | Biology |
| 10. | DNA | 20. | North Star |

# Quiz 20: Religion

1. Who in 2013 became the first pope to resign in 600 years?

2. In the Christian calendar, what name is given to the Sunday immediately prior to Easter Sunday?

3. Members of which religion would wear a hijab?

4. What is the first book of the Old Testament?

5. Shinto is the indigenous religion of which Asian country?

6. Lambeth Palace is the official London residence of which religious leader?

7. A gurdwara is a place of worship for followers of which religion?

8. Which word links an order of mammals that includes monkeys and apes and a title given to some bishops?

9. What Christian festival is celebrated on 6 January?

10. Who is the Supreme Governor of the Church of England?

11. According to the 2011 census, what is the second largest religion in the UK after Christianity?

12. Purim, Yom Kippur, and Hanukkah are festivals in which religion?

13. What was the name of the Roman governor who authorized the crucifixion of Jesus Christ?

14. Who said, 'The love of money is the root of all evil'?

15. Hajj is a pilgrimage carried out by Muslims to which city?

16. Who succeeded Rowan Williams as Archbishop of Canterbury in February 2013?

17. Diwali is a festival in which religion?

18. What are members of the Church of Jesus Christ of Latter-day Saints more commonly known as?

19. According to the 2011 census, 176,632 people in England and Wales described their religion as what?
    a) Jedi
    b) Klingon
    c) Satanist

20. Which day marks the start of Lent?
    a) Ash Tuesday
    b) Ash Wednesday
    c) Ash Thursday

## Answers to Quiz 19: Pot Luck

1. Dublin
2. Quentin Tarantino
3. George Washington
4. Mona Lisa
5. Faith
6. The Queen
7. Brazil
8. The Pope
9. Rio de Janeiro
10. Nevada
11. Gerard Depardieu
12. Aintree
13. English and French
14. Israel
15. Harry Potter and the Philosopher's Stone
16. Italy
17. White
18. Barcelona
19. Eat it
20. Looper

# Quiz 21: Pot Luck

1. According to the proverb, what is the spice of life?

2. Which spooky celebration takes place each year on 31 October?

3. Which object represents Ireland on the flag known as the Royal Standard?

4. Which film director directed the 2012 Olympic Games opening ceremony?

5. Which sport is known in Italy as 'calcio'?

6. Who was the last British monarch from the House of Hanover?

7. What do the initials HMRC stand for?

8. Which German team did Chelsea beat in the final of the 2012 Champions League?

9. Which pair host the TV show 'Saturday Night Takeaway'?

10. What name is given to the wife of a marquis?

11. The films 'Casino' and 'Ocean's Eleven' are set in which American city?

12. Ben Ainslie is a multiple Olympic gold-medal-winner in which sport?

13. In addition to white, a bride traditionally wears something of what colour?

14. 'Harpo' is the name of which actress and talk-show host's production company?

15. In UK politics, on which day of the week does prime minister's questions take place?

16. The Sorbonne is a university in which city?

17. Carol Klein, Anna Fowler, and Monty Don regularly present TV programmes on which subject?

18. Which supermarket is the food division of the John Lewis Partnership?

19. What nationality was the polar explorer Roald Amundsen?
   a) Danish
   b) German
   c) Norwegian

20. Who was America's longest-serving president?
   a) Theodore Roosevelt
   b) Franklin D Roosevelt
   c) Ronald Reagan

EASY

## Answers to Quiz 20: Religion

1. Benedict XVI (Joseph Ratzinger)
2. Palm Sunday
3. Islam
4. Genesis
5. Japan
6. The Archbishop of Canterbury
7. Sikhism
8. Primate
9. Epiphany
10. The Queen
11. Islam
12. Judaism
13. Pontius Pilate
14. St Paul
15. Mecca
16. Justin Welby
17. Hinduism
18. Mormons
19. Jedi
20. Ash Wednesday

# Quiz 22: Politics

1. Who was elected for a second term as US President in 2012?

2. In which decade was the United Nations founded?

3. Which organization carries out the practical and administrative work of the government?

4. Who was the British prime minister from 1979 until 1990?

5. Which British politicial leader is married to Justine Thornton?

6. In 2012 François Hollande was elected president of which country?

7. Which Respect Party politician appeared on 'Celebrity Big Brother'?

8. What department is responsible for the British government's financial and economic policy?

9. The first televised debate featuring British party leaders took place in the run-up to the general election in which year?

10. Whom did David Cameron succeed as leader of the Conservative Party?

11. In British politics, what are the four great offices of state?

12. True or false – the Chancellor of the Exchequer can drink alcohol while delivering the Budget speech?

13. Which UK government department has the initials FCO?

14. Which word describes the transfer of power from a central body to a regional body?

15. Which political leader lives at 1600 Pennsylvania Avenue?

16. Nigel Farage is the leader of which political party?

17. How often do elections to the Scottish Parliament take place?

18. 11 Downing Street is the official residence of the holder of which post?

19. What did the F in John F Kennedy stand for?
    a) Fitzgerald
    b) Francis
    c) Frederick

20. How many elected MPs are in the House of Commons?
    a) 550
    b) 650
    c) 750

## Answers to Quiz 21: Pot Luck

1. Variety
2. Halloween
3. Harp
4. Danny Boyle
5. Football
6. Queen Victoria
7. Her Majesty's Revenue and Customs
8. Bayern Munich
9. Ant and Dec
10. Marchioness
11. Las Vegas
12. Sailing
13. Blue
14. Oprah Winfrey
15. Wednesday
16. Paris
17. Gardening
18. Waitrose
19. Norwegian
20. Franklin D Roosevelt

# Quiz 23: Pot Luck

1. In rhyming slang, what is referred to as the Oxo?

2. Which Olympic gymnast won TV's 'Dancing On Ice' in 2013?

3. Who is the host of comedy panel show 'Celebrity Juice'?

4. Three cricketers from which country were jailed in 2011 for their part in a betting scandal?

5. Who was Germany's first female Chancellor?

6. Which music TV show, first screened in 1964, was broadcast for the last time in July 2006?

7. England were dumped out of the 2010 World Cup after being thrashed 4-1 by which country?

8. In which part of the British Isles is Tynwald Day celebrated?

9. What is the best possible hand in a game of Texas hold 'em poker?

10. Proverbially, a change is as good as what?

11. In cricket, what do the initials LBW stand for?

12. Who is the youngest of the Queen's four children?

13. Who is the male professional baker on TV show 'The Great British Bake Off'?

14. Who succeeded Chris Moyles as presenter of the Radio 1 Breakfast Show?

15. The Tamil Tigers were a separatist movement in which country?

16. 'Nemo me impune lacessit' (No one provokes me with impunity) is the motto of which part of the UK?

Answers – page 49

17. Ken Bruce, Steve Wright, and Jeremy Vine are presenters on which national radio station?

18. Which country covers a bigger area – the UK or Norway?

19. Tennis star Rafael Nadal is from which country?
    a) France
    b) Italy
    c) Spain

20. What is the Secret Intelligence Service also known as?
    a) CI5
    b) MI5
    c) MI6

## Answers to Quiz 22: Politics

1. Barack Obama
2. 1940s
3. The Civil Service
4. Margaret Thatcher
5. Ed Miliband
6. France
7. George Galloway
8. The Treasury
9. 2010
10. Michael Howard
11. Prime Minister, Chancellor of the Exchequer, Foreign Secretary, and Home Secretary
12. True
13. Foreign and Commonwealth Office
14. Devolution
15. The President of the USA
16. UKIP
17. Every four years
18. The Chancellor of the Exchequer
19. Fitzgerald
20. 650

# Quiz 24: Scotland

1. What is the capital city of Scotland?

2. Who became First Minister of Scotland in 2007 and again in 2011?

3. Which Scottish city will host the 2014 Commonwealth Games?

4. Which stadium is the home of the Scottish national football team?

5. Haggis is made from which animal?

6. Which Brit Award winning singer, who was raised in Aberdeenshire, sang at the opening and closing ceremonies of the London 2012 Olympics?

7. Pittodrie is the home ground of which football team?

8. Which Kirkcaldy-born philosopher and economist wrote 'The Wealth of Nations'?

9. The Duke and Duchess of Cambridge met while studying at which Scottish university?

10. Which poet is known as The Bard of Ayrshire?

11. True or false – Scotland has the highest proportion of red-haired people in the world?

12. Which Scottish place has the nickname of 'The Granite City'?

13. Which Scottish author created the fictional detective Inspector Rebus?

14. Heriot-Watt University is in which Scottish city?

15. Which city lies between the River Dee and the River Don?

16. Who was appointed manager of the Scottish national football team in January 2013?

17. Which Scot has won the most Olympic gold medals by a British competitor?

18. What is the Gaelic word for Scotland?

19. DC Thomson, the publisher of 'The Beano' and 'The Dandy' is based in which city?
    a) Aberdeen
    b) Dundee
    c) Edinburgh

20. What sort of establishment is Barlinnie?
    a) luxury hotel
    b) football ground
    c) prison

## Answers to Quiz 23: Pot Luck

1. The Tube
2. Beth Tweddle
3. Keith Lemon
4. Pakistan
5. Angela Merkel
6. Top of the Pops
7. Germany
8. The Isle of Man
9. Royal flush
10. A rest
11. Leg Before Wicket
12. Prince Edward
13. Paul Hollywood
14. Nick Grimshaw
15. Sri Lanka
16. Scotland
17. Radio 2
18. Norway
19. Spain
20. MI6

# Quiz 25: Pot Luck

EASY

1.  What is the last book in the Harry Potter series?

2.  In cricket, if a batsman is dismissed for a duck, how many runs have they scored?

3.  In which year did England last host football's World Cup?

4.  Who was the MP for Sedgefield from 1983 until 2007?

5.  What sort of BBC programmes are presented by Alex Deakin, Carol Kirkwood, and Helen Willetts?

6.  Hugh Laurie played the lead character in which US medical drama?

7.  Jason Maguire, Paul Carberry, and Ruby Walsh are notable names in which sport?

8.  Commissioner Gordon is a close ally of which comic-book superhero?

9.  Bela Lugosi, Christopher Lee, and Gary Oldman have all played which creepy film character?

10. 'The Best is Yet to Come' is written on the grave of which legendary crooner?

11. Lex Luthor is the arch-nemesis of which comic-book and film superhero?

12. Hearts and Hibernian are football clubs in which British city?

13. What is the bone called the scapula more commonly known as?

14. Castel Gandolfo is the summer retreat of which religious leader?

15. What sort of dessert is associated with the Black Forest region?

16. Which British artist staged 11 simultaneous exhibitions of his 'spot' paintings in 2012?

17. Which Midlands town also appears in the title of a novel by Jane Austen?

18. Which three colours feature on the flags of both Germany and Belgium?

19. A sonnet is a poem made up of how many lines?
    a) 4
    b) 14
    c) 24

20. The tibia is located in which part of the body?
    a) arm
    b) ear
    c) leg

## Answers to Quiz 24: Scotland

1. Edinburgh
2. Alex Salmond
3. Glasgow
4. Hampden Park
5. Sheep
6. Emeli Sandè
7. Aberdeen
8. Adam Smith
9. St Andrews
10. Robert Burns
11. True
12. Aberdeen
13. Ian Rankin
14. Edinburgh
15. Aberdeen
16. Gordon Strachan
17. Sir Chris Hoy
18. Alba
19. Dundee
20. Prison

# Quiz 26: Sport part 1

1. Which British athlete won gold at the 2012 Olympics in the heptathlon?

2. 'The Rocket' is the nickname of which snooker player?

3. Lord's is the English headquarters of which sport?

4. Which Northern Irish golfer won the US Open in 2011 and the US PGA in 2012?

5. Which country won football's World Cup in 2010 and the European Championship in 2008 and 2012?

6. Ellie Simmonds is a gold-medal-winning athlete in which Paralympic sport?

7. How often does golf's Ryder Cup take place?

8. Who was the first foreign manager of the England football team?

9. Which German won the Formula One Drivers' Championship in 2010, 2011, and 2012?

10. Which Ivorian striker scored the winning goal for Chelsea in the 2012 Champions League final?

11. In rugby union, what number shirt is worn by the full back?

12. Which of the four tennis grand slam events takes place latest in the year?

13. Which football team was demoted to the bottom tier of Scottish football in 2012 after going into liquidation?

14. Which seven-time world champion retired from snooker after a quarter-final defeat at the 2012 championships?

15. The All-England Tennis Club is located in which London suburb?

16. Which two countries hosted football's 2012 European Championship?

17. Dale Steyn, Morne Morkel, and AB de Villiers play international cricket for which country?

18. How many players make up a rugby league team?

19. Which team broke the men's 4x100m athletics world record at the 2012 Olympics?
    a) Jamaica
    b) Trinidad and Tobago
    c) USA

20. Who succeeded Andrew Strauss as captain of the England cricket team?
    a) Ian Bell
    b) Alastair Cook
    c) Jonathan Trott

## Answers to Quiz 25: Pot Luck

1.  Harry Potter and the Deathly Hallows
2.  0
3.  1966
4.  Tony Blair
5.  Weather forecasts
6.  House
7.  Horse racing
8.  Batman
9.  Dracula
10. Frank Sinatra
11. Superman
12. Edinburgh
13. Shoulder blade
14. The Pope
15. Gateau
16. Damien Hirst
17. Mansfield (Park)
18. Black, yellow, and red
19. 14
20. Leg

# Quiz 27: Pot Luck

1. Sachin Tendulkar played international cricket for which country?

2. According to the proverb, you cannot have your what and eat it?

3. 'He's not the Messiah, he's a very naughty boy' is a line from which 1979 cult comedy?

4. The Wedgwood Museum is in which English Midlands city?

5. 'Waiting For Godot' and 'Endgame' are plays by which Irish playwright?

6. Who was elected president of Russia for a third time in March 2012?

7. Which technology guru died of cancer, aged 56, on 5 October 2012?

8. Which British actress played Nanny McPhee in the 2005 film of the same name?

9. In June 2011, Sepp Blatter was re-elected for a fourth time as president of which sporting organization?

10. Which is the only tennis grand slam event that is played on grass?

11. What does the acronym BAFTA stand for?

12. Which word that describes a member of the dog family is also a type of tooth?

13. The pasta sauce bolognese originates from which Italian city?

14. What name connects a famous explorer and the film director who made 'Harry Potter and the Chamber of Secrets'?

15. Which two colours feature on the flags of Austria, Poland, and Denmark?

16. Which Irish comedian hosts the panel show 'Mock the Week'?

17. Which band recorded the 1960s classic album 'Pet Sounds'?

18. Which Hollywood A-lister played Dr Doug Ross in US medical drama ER?

19. In which field is Rankin a notable figure?
    a) architecture
    b) photography
    c) sculpture

20. How many books are there in the Harry Potter series?
    a) six
    b) seven
    c) eight

## Answers to Quiz 26: Sport part 1

1. Jessica Ennis
2. Ronnie O'Sullivan
3. Cricket
4. Rory McIlroy
5. Spain
6. Swimming
7. Every two years
8. Sven-Göran Eriksson
9. Sebastian Vettel
10. Didier Drogba
11. 15
12. US Open
13. Rangers
14. Stephen Hendry
15. Wimbledon
16. Poland and Ukraine
17. South Africa
18. 13
19. Jamaica
20. Alastair Cook

# Quiz 28: Starts with the Same Letter

1. Who is the comedy partner of Ben Miller and the host of the TV quiz show 'Pointless'?

2. Which actor wrote the classic boxing film 'Rocky'?

3. Who is the host of TV comedy 'TV Burp'?

4. Which British heavyweight champion of the world won gold for Canada at the 1988 Olympic Games?

5. Which actor, known for his booming voice, played Prince Vultan in the camp classic 'Flash Gordon'?

6. What was the title of Abba's second UK number one hit?

7. Norma Jeane Mortenson was the real name of which Hollywood icon?

8. Greendale is the setting for which long-running children's animation series?

9. Which actor became a Hollywood star through his screen persona 'the Tramp'?

10. Which actor played Dave Lister in sci-fi comedy 'Red Dwarf' and Lloyd Mullaney in 'Coronation Street'?

11. Which Australian feminist wrote 'The Female Eunuch'?

12. Which Respect Party politician was elected MP in the Bradford West by-election in 2012?

13. Which former member of pop group Atomic Kitten went on to win 'I'm a Celebrity ... Get Me out of Here' in 2004?

14. 'Voice of an Angel' was the debut album by which Welsh singer?

15. Who won the men's singles at Wimbledon in 1985 at the age of just 17?

16. Which actress found fame playing Catherine Tramell in the 1992 thriller 'Basic Instinct'?

17. Which composer's works include the 'Enigma Variations' and 'Pomp and Circumstance Marches'?

18. What was the magician and illusionist Ehrich Weiss better known as?

19. 'Brighton Rock', 'The Heart of the Matter', 'The Third Man', and 'The Quiet American' are novels by which English author?

20. The Sundance Film Festival was founded by which actor and film director?

## Answers to Quiz 27: Pot Luck

1. India
2. Cake
3. Monty Python's Life of Brian
4. Stoke-on-Trent
5. Samuel Beckett
6. Vladimir Putin
7. Steve Jobs
8. Emma Thompson
9. FIFA
10. Wimbledon
11. British Academy of Film and Television Arts
12. Canine
13. Bologna
14. Christopher Columbus
15. Red and white
16. Dara O Briain
17. The Beach Boys
18. George Clooney
19. Photography
20. Seven

# Quiz 29: Pot Luck

1. Which girl's name is also the title of a novel by Jane Austen?

2. What is the capital of the Isle of Man?

3. Which team was beaten in the final of the 2010 FIFA World Cup?

4. In law, what do the initials CPS stand for?

5. Charles Lynton are the middle names of which former British prime minister?

6. According to a survey by Goal.com, who was the world's richest footballer in 2013?

7. Extremadura, Galicia, and Asturias are regions of which European country?

8. What is the Italian city Firenze known as in English?

9. What is the longest bone in the human body?

10. Which American playwright wrote 'A Streetcar Named Desire' and 'Cat on a Hot Tin Roof'?

11. What Portuguese island group is also the name of a type of sponge cake?

12. Enchiladas, tacos, and tortillas are associated with the cuisine of which country?

13. Which country is larger – France or Italy?

14. München is the local name for which city?

15. What is the second largest planet of the solar system?

16. Which name describes a triangle that is made up of three sides of equal length?

17. The San Siro Stadium is in which Italian city?

18. The food 'sashimi' is a speciality of which country?

19. The fibula is a bone in which part of the human body?
    a) arm
    b) leg
    c) skull

20. In which century was the artist Michelangelo born?
    a) 15th
    b) 16th
    c) 17th

## Answers to Quiz 28: Starts with the Same Letter

1. Alexander Armstrong
2. Sylvester Stallone
3. Harry Hill
4. Lennox Lewis
5. Brian Blessed
6. Mamma Mia!
7. Marilyn Monroe
8. Postman Pat
9. Charlie Chaplin
10. Craig Charles
11. Germaine Greer
12. George Galloway
13. Kerry Katona
14. Charlotte Church
15. Boris Becker
16. Sharon Stone
17. Edward Elgar
18. Harry Houdini
19. Graham Greene
20. Robert Redford

# Quiz 30: Wales

1. Which three colours appear on the Welsh flag?

2. Which Swansea-born star won a Best Supporting Actress Oscar in 2003 for her performance in 'Chicago'?

3. At which stadium does the Welsh national rugby union team play its home matches?

4. Which celebration takes place in Wales each year on 1 March?

5. Which Welsh actor played Batman in the 2012 film 'The Dark Knight Rises'?

6. The Duke and Duchess of Cambridge live on which Welsh island?

7. True or false – sci-fi drama 'Dr Who' is filmed in Cardiff?

8. Who was the first Welsh team to play in football's Premier League?

9. What is the highest mountain in Wales?

10. Which actor and comedian, who rose to fame in the TV comedy 'Marion and Geoff', is famous for his 'small man in a box' voice?

11. Which vegetable is a national symbol of Wales?

12. What is the second largest city in Wales by population?

13. Who was the first Welsh prime minister of the United Kingdom?

14. What is the Welsh national anthem, 'Hen Wlad Fy Nhadau', known as in English?

15. Which sporting event was hosted in Wales for the first time at the Celtic Manor Resort, Newport, in 2010?

16. TV sitcom 'Gavin and Stacey' was set in which Welsh town?

17. What town, famous for its bookshops, is known in Welsh as Y Gelli?

18. First held in 1176, what is the name of the annual Welsh festival of literature, music, and performance?

19. There is a Welsh-speaking community in which South American country?
    a) Argentina
    b) Chile
    c) Colombia

20. Which of the following is an area of Cardiff?
    a) Lion Bay
    b) Snake Bay
    c) Tiger Bay

## Answers to Quiz 29: Pot Luck

1. Emma
2. Douglas
3. The Netherlands
4. Crown Prosecution Service
5. Tony Blair
6. David Beckham
7. Spain
8. Florence
9. Femur (thigh bone)
10. Tennessee Williams
11. Madeira
12. Mexico
13. France
14. Munich
15. Saturn
16. Equilateral
17. Milan
18. Japan
19. Leg
20. 15th

# Quiz 31: Pot Luck

EASY

1. Which pair host the TV show 'I'm a Celebrity ... Get Me out of Here'?

2. Which Russian novelist wrote 'War and Peace' and 'Anna Karenina'?

3. How many ribs does a human have?

4. Which American singer accidentally drowned on the day before the 2012 Grammy Awards, at the age of just 48?

5. The cerebrum is the largest portion of which organ of the human body?

6. Proverbially, what is next to godliness?

7. Tabsaco sauce takes its name from a region of which country?

8. Battle cruiser is Cockney rhyming slang for what type of establishment?

9. Cardiology is the branch of medicine that deals with which part of the body?

10. True or false – facial hair is banned in North Korea?

11. Alphabetically, what is the first colour in a rainbow?

12. Who wrote the best selling novel 'Fifty Shades of Grey'?

13. Who made his 1000th appearance for Manchester United in March 2013?

14. Which city, famous for its bull run, is the capital of the Spanish region of Navarre?

15. What are the three primary colours of light?

16. In computing, what is an ISP?

17. Which two seas are linked by the Suez Canal?

18. Which 'Harry Potter' actor had the lead role in the 2012 film 'The Woman in Black'?

19. On a football pitch, how far is the penalty spot from the goal line?
    a) 10 yards
    b) 11 yards
    c) 12 yards

20. What is the name of the main circuit board of a computer?
    a) brotherboard
    b) fatherboard
    c) motherboard

## Answers to Quiz 30: Wales

1. Green, white, and red
2. Catherine Zeta-Jones
3. Millennium Stadium, Cardiff
4. St David's Day
5. Christian Bale
6. Anglesey
7. True
8. Swansea City
9. Snowdon
10. Rob Brydon
11. The leek
12. Swansea
13. David Lloyd George
14. Land of my Fathers
15. The Ryder Cup
16. Barry
17. Hay-on-Wye
18. National Eisteddfod
19. Argentina
20. Tiger Bay

# Quiz 32: Europe

EASY

1. Which European capital is also known as 'The Eternal City'?

2. In 2013, Queen Beatrix abdicated as monarch of which country?

3. The Reichstag is the parliament of which country?

4. What is Europe's highest active volcano?

5. Wallonia is a region of which European country?

6. The Bois de Boulogne is a famous park in which European capital?

7. Aarhus is the second largest city in which country?

8. What are the two independent states that lie within the borders of Italy?

9. Belgium shares borders with which four countries?

10. Which country shares land borders with Norway, Russia, and Sweden?

11. Picardie, Limousin, and Alsace are regions of which country?

12. Designed by Frank Gehry, the Guggenheim Museum is in which European city?

13. What is the English name of the city that the Germans call Köln?

14. The Rialto Bridge is in which Italian city?

15. What are the five European countries to have won football's World Cup?

16. What is the second largest city in the Republic of Ireland?

17. Pop acts Basshunter, The Cardigans, Ace of Base, and Roxette are from which country?

18. El Prat Airport serves which major European city?

19. Tallinn is the largest city in which country?
    a) Estonia
    b) Latvia
    c) Lithuania

20. Which of these countries was not a founder member of the European Union?
    a) Belgium
    b) Luxembourg
    c) Republic of Ireland

EASY

## Answers to Quiz 31: Pot Luck

1. Ant and Dec
2. Leo Tolstoy
3. 24
4. Whitney Houston
5. The brain
6. Cleanliness
7. Mexico
8. Pub
9. The heart
10. True
11. Blue
12. EL James
13. Ryan Giggs
14. Pamplona
15. Red, green, and blue
16. Internet service provider
17. Red Sea and Mediterranean Sea
18. Daniel Radcliffe
19. 12 yards
20. Motherboard

# Quiz 33: Pot Luck

EASY

1. Complete the proverb: 'nothing ventured, nothing ...'

2. Which American city is nicknamed Sin City?

3. Who was the first South Korean artist to top the UK singles chart?

4. What was the name of the chart-topping song?

5. Who wrote the novel 'Sense and Sensibility'?

6. What type of headgear is usually awarded to players appearing in a sport for their country?

7. St Mary's is the home ground of which English football team?

8. Who are the biggest selling female group in pop history?

9. Grandmaster is used to describe a very strong player of which game?

10. Which sportswear brand was invented by German Adolf Dassler?

11. James Arthur won what 2012 TV talent show?

12. Österreich is the local name for which country?

13. Which English author's only novel was 'Wuthering Heights'?

14. The Royal Shakespeare Company is based in which Midlands town?

15. Which Italian composer's name translates into English as Joseph Green?

16. 'The Twits', 'Matilda', and 'The BFG' are children's books by which author?

Answers – page 69

17. The bands UB40 and Duran Duran are from which British city?

18. According to legend, who was struck blind after looking at Lady Godiva?

19. What is the name of the wife of former US President George W Bush?
a) Hillary
b) Laura
c) Michelle

20. Which Olympian won 'Strictly Come Dancing' in 2012?
a) Victoria Pendleton
b) Louis Smith
c) Beth Tweddle

## Answers to Quiz 32: Europe

1. Rome
2. The Netherlands
3. Germany
4. Mount Etna
5. Belgium
6. Paris
7. Denmark
8. San Marino and the Vatican City
9. France, Germany, Luxembourg, and the Netherlands
10. Finland
11. France
12. Bilbao
13. Cologne
14. Venice
15. England, France, Germany, Italy, and Spain
16. Cork
17. Sweden
18. Barcelona
19. Estonia
20. Republic of Ireland

# Quiz 34: Television

1. On the TV quiz show 'QI', what do the initials QI stand for?

2. Which broadcasting veteran celebrated '60 Years In The Wild' in 2012?

3. Which pair played PJ and Duncan in the children's TV drama 'Byker Grove'?

4. What is the first name of Mrs Brown of 'Mrs Brown's Boys' fame?

5. Who is the host of the home improvement show 'Property Ladder'?

6. Which TV soap celebrated its 40th anniversary in October 2012?

7. Detective drama 'Scott and Bailey' is set in which British city?

8. 'Cooking doesn't get any tougher than this' is a catchphrase from which culinary TV show?

9. Nick Hancock, Paul Merton, and Frank Skinner have all hosted which TV show?

10. Who are the presenters of the TV talent show 'The Voice'?

11. 'Holby City' is a spin-off series from which British drama?

12. Margo and Jerry Leadbetter were characters in which classic comedy?

13. Which TV soap was broadcast for the first time on 19 February 1985?

14. What was the name of the TV diving show featuring Tom Daley and a group of celebrities?

Answers – page 71

15. Which pop star turned physics professor hosted the TV science shows 'Wonders of the Solar System' and 'Wonders of the Universe'?

16. Diags, Gemma Collins, and Lucy Mecklenburgh are characters in which reality TV show?

17. Who plays the title character in the ITV drama 'Doc Martin'?

18. 'To me, to you' is a catchphrase from which children's TV comedy duo?

19. Which TV soap is set in Erinsborough?
    a) Hollyoaks
    b) Home and Away
    c) Neighbours

20. Which TV station aired for the first time in 1997?
    a) Channel 4
    b) Channel 5
    c) Sky Sports

EASY

## Answers to Quiz 33: Pot Luck

1. Gained
2. Las Vegas
3. Psy
4. Gangnam Style
5. Jane Austen
6. Cap
7. Southampton
8. The Spice Girls
9. Chess
10. Adidas
11. The X Factor
12. Austria
13. Emily Brontë
14. Stratford-upon-Avon
15. Giuseppe Verdi
16. Roald Dahl
17. Birmingham
18. Peeping Tom
19. Laura
20. Louis Smith

# Quiz 35: Pot Luck

1. What is the smallest planet in the Solar System?

2. Which tax has the initials CGT?

3. What is the name of the short stick used by a conductor to direct an orchestra or choir?

4. Which hit musical was set in a school called Rydell High?

5. Which legendary crooner was nicknamed 'Chairman of the Broad'?

6. 'Ruby' is rhyming slang for what type of food?

7. Shylock the money lender is a character in which Shakespeare play?

8. What was the first name of 'Dad's Army' character Captain Mainwaring?

9. What is the motto of the Boy Scouts?

10. Which condiment features in the title of an album by The Beatles?

11. Mount Fuji is the largest mountain of which country?

12. Which Oscar-winning actress played Tallulah in the 1976 film musical 'Bugsy Malone'?

13. Which ocean is larger than all the world's continents combined?

14. Which actor plays the magical TV detective Jonathan Creek?

15. In the UK in which month is the shortest day of the year?

16. How many strings are on a standard bass guitar?

17. The mouth of the River Amazon is in which country?

18. In America it's called cotton candy but what is it known as in the UK?

19. Which two-word Latin phrase means 'to excess'?
    a) ad nauseam
    b) al fresco
    c) ab initio

20. Which of the following is a college at Oxford University?
    a) St Hilda's
    b) St Betty's
    c) St Stella's

EASY

## Answers to Quiz 34: Television

1. Quite Interesting
2. David Attenborough
3. Ant and Dec
4. Agnes
5. Sarah Beeny
6. Emmerdale
7. Manchester
8. Masterchef
9. Room 101
10. Reggie Yates and Holly Willoughby
11. Casualty
12. The Good Life
13. EastEnders
14. Splash
15. Brian Cox
16. The Only Way Is Essex
17. Martin Clunes
18. The Chuckle Brothers
19. Neighbours
20. Channel 5

# Quiz 36: Olympic Games

EASY

1. Victorian Pendleton was an Olympic gold medallist in which sport?

2. Mo Farah won gold in the 2012 games at which two events?

3. Which British swimmer won gold in the 400m and 800m freestyle at the 2008 games?

4. Which American sprinter became the first man to win gold in both the 200m and 400m at the 1996 games?

5. The Searle Brothers won gold for Great Britain in 1992 in which sport?

6. Which city will host the 2016 Olympic Games?

7. Which sprinter was disqualified from the final of the men's 100m in 1988 after failing a drug test?

8. 'The Bird's Nest' was the nickname given to the Olympic stadium in which city?

9. In 1992, a team representing the USA at which sport was dubbed 'The Dream Team'?

10. Which British athlete won gold in the 400m at the Beijing games?

11. Which football team are set to move into the London Olympic Stadium in 2016?

12. Who said, 'It's what I came here to do; I'm now a legend' after winning his second gold medal of London 2012?

13. In which Olympic sport can a competitor win by scoring an ippon?

14. Which British athlete won gold in the 800m and 1500m at the 2004 Olympic Games?

15. True or false – the hammer is an event in the Olympic decathlon?

16. Which politician was left hanging in mid-air while riding a zip wire as part of the London 2012 Olympic celebrations?

17. Which British athlete won the men's 1500m race at the 1980 and 1984 Olympics?

18. What colour is the outer ring of an Olympic archery target?

19. Jessica Ennis was born in which city?
    a) Leeds
    b) Manchester
    c) Sheffield

20. What was the first Australian city to host the Olympic Games?
    a) Brisbane
    b) Melbourne
    c) Sydney

**EASY**

## Answers to Quiz 35: Pot Luck

1. Mercury
2. Capital Gains Tax
3. Baton
4. Grease
5. Frank Sinatra
6. Curry
7. The Merchant of Venice
8. George
9. Be Prepared
10. Pepper
11. Japan
12. Jodie Foster
13. Pacific
14. Alan Davies
15. December
16. Four
17. Brazil
18. Candy floss
19. Ad nauseam
20. St Hilda's

# Quiz 37: Pot Luck

1. What are the three United Nations member states whose name starts with the letter J?

2. Which 2012 event had the motto 'Inspire a generation'?

3. What is the text of an opera called?

4. An invertebrate is an animal that lacks what?

5. Noel and Liam Gallagher are famous fans of which English football club?

6. What is the only capital city of a European Union country that starts with the letter D?

7. 'Floreat Etona' is the motto of which famous school?

8. In relation to the medical condition, what do the initials ADHD stand for?

9. Which part of the body is also the name of the band that recorded the albums 'The Seldom Seen Kid' and 'Build a Rocket Boys!'?

10. The LSE is a university based in which city?

11. Which European football team plays its home games at the Nou Camp?

12. Kingston is the capital city of which Caribbean country?

13. 'Circle of Life', 'Grasslands Chant', and 'Can You Feel the Love?' are songs from which film-turned-West End musical?

14. Robin is the sidekick of which superhero?

15. 'Decus et tutamen' is inscribed on the edge of which British coin?

16. If the countries of the European Union were listed alphabetically, which would be last on the list?

17. The airline Qantas is based in which country?

18. Which band topped the UK singles charts in the 1980s with 'Relax', 'Two Tribes', and 'The Power of Love'?

19. Who were the first country to win football's World Cup five times?
    a) Brazil
    b) Germany
    c) Italy

20. Which of the following is a character in Shakespeare's 'Twelfth Night'?
    a) Toby Belch
    b) Toby Burp
    c) Toby Trump

## Answers to Quiz 36: Olympic Games

| | | | |
|---|---|---|---|
| 1. | Cycling | 11. | West Ham United |
| 2. | 5000m and 10,000m | 12. | Usain Bolt |
| 3. | Rebecca Adlington | 13. | Judo |
| 4. | Michael Johnson | 14. | Dame Kelly Holmes |
| 5. | Rowing | 15. | False |
| 6. | Rio de Janeiro | 16. | Boris Johnson |
| 7. | Ben Johnson | 17. | Sebastian Coe |
| 8. | Beijing | 18. | White |
| 9. | Basketball | 19. | Sheffield |
| 10. | Christine Ohuruogu | 20. | Melbourne in 1956 |

# Quiz 38: Animals

1. Ornithology is the scientific study of what type of animals?

2. Which animal is known proverbially as the 'king of the beasts'?

3. Which word is used for an animal that feeds on plants rather than meat?

4. Durham, Jersey, and Angus are breeds of what type of hoofed animal?

5. What type of creature is a natterjack?

6. The chimpanzee is native to which continent?

7. How many legs does a spider have?

8. Arabian and Bactrian are types of which large ruminant?

9. What is a male duck called?

10. What is the largest living bird?

11. Which bird is the emblem of the USA?

12. Which English football team is nicknamed the Rams?

13. Caribou is an alternative name for which animal?

14. The tiger is native to which continent?

15. A fawn is the name given to the young of which animal?

16. What is the fastest four-footed animal on earth?

17. Which boy's name is also the word used to describe the young of a kangaroo?

18. What is the young of a goat called?

19. Where do penguins live?
    a) North Pole
    b) South Pole
    c) both

20. What type of creature is a chinchilla?
    a) ape
    b) bird
    c) rodent

EASY

## Answers to Quiz 37: Pot Luck

1. Jamaica, Japan, and Jordan
2. The London Olympics
3. Libretto
4. A backbone
5. Manchester City
6. Dublin
7. Eton
8. Attention deficit hyperactivity disorder
9. Elbow
10. London
11. Barcelona
12. Jamaica
13. The Lion King
14. Batman
15. £1
16. United Kingdom
17. Australia
18. Frankie Goes to Hollywood
19. Brazil
20. Toby Belch

# Quiz 39: Pot Luck

1. Bayern is the local name for which state of Germany?

2. R-Patz is the nickname of which Hollywood star?

3. In London, what are the Dominion, Phoenix, and Vaudeville?

4. Who are the three hosts of the TV programme 'Top Gear'?

5. People in which profession are associated with Savile Row?

6. Who was Scrooge's former business partner in 'A Christmas Carol'?

7. 'Little Things' was a number one single in 2012 by which popular boy band?

8. Which former Tory MP partnered Anton du Beke on TV talent show 'Strictly Come Dancing'?

9. What is the only capital city of a European Union country that starts with the letter M?

10. The three witches are central characters in which Shakespeare play?

11. What are the names of Margaret Thatcher's twin children?

12. By what name is the 16th-century French astrologer Michel de Notre Dame better known?

13. Who wrote the long-running West End play 'The Mousetrap'?

14. French emperor Napoleon Bonaparte was born on which island?

15. Complete the proverb: 'When the going gets tough, the tough ...'

16. Home to a famous festival, La Croisette is a prominent road in which French resort?

17. In which sport would a competitor perform a clean and jerk?

18. What are the three European Union countries that start with the letter L?

19. Which of the following is an American political movement?
a) The Coffee Party
b) The Tea Party
c) The Sugar Party

20. In which year did South Africa host football's World Cup?
a) 2006
b) 2008
c) 2010

**EASY**

## Answers to Quiz 38: Animals

1. Birds
2. Lion
3. Herbivore
4. Cattle
5. Toad
6. Africa
7. Eight
8. Camel
9. Drake
10. Ostrich
11. The American (or Bald) Eagle
12. Derby County
13. Reindeer
14. Asia
15. Deer
16. Cheetah
17. Joey
18. Kid
19. South Pole
20. Rodent

# Quiz 40: Connections part 1

1. What was the title of Clive Dunn's 1970 number one hit single?

2. Who served as president of South Africa from 1994 until 1999?

3. What was the name of Queen Victoria's husband?

4. 'Layla' was the only UK top ten single from which band?

5. In London, what are Smithfield, Borough, Portobello, and Old Billingsgate?

6. Who was the first English footballer to be sold for a transfer fee of £1 million?

7. What is the nickname of Bolton Wanderers FC?

8. What is the name of the main character in 'The Omen' series of horror films?

9. What was the name of the horse ridden by 'Ernie (The Fastest Milkman in the West)'?

10. Which word is used to represent the letter M in the NATO Phonetic Alphabet?

11. In Greek mythology, whose beauty caused Apollo to grant her the gift of prophecy?

12. Which word describes a branched, decorative ceiling-mounted light fixture?

13. Labour politician Harriet Harman is the MP for which constituency?

14. What was the name of the character played by Sarah Lancashire in the TV soap 'Coronation Street'?

15. Which actor played Bob Ferris is the TV comedies 'The Likely Lads' and 'Whatever Happened to the Likely Lads'?

16. Which German-born actress and singer appears on the cover of The Beatles' album 'Sergeant Pepper's Lonely Hearts Club Band'?

17. Released in 1982, what was Toni Basil's only UK hit single?

18. What was the maiden name of the character played by Jessie Wallace in 'EastEnders'?

19. 'We All Had Doctors' Papers' was a number one album by which Welsh folk singer and comedian?

20. What is the connection between all the answers?

EASY

## Answers to Quiz 39: Pot Luck

1. Bavaria
2. Robert Pattinson
3. West End theatres
4. Jeremy Clarkson, James May, and Richard Hammond
5. Tailors
6. Jacob Marley
7. One Direction
8. Ann Widdecombe
9. Madrid
10. Macbeth
11. Mark and Carol
12. Nostradamus
13. Agatha Christie
14. Corsica
15. Get going
16. Cannes
17. Weightlifting
18. Latvia, Lithuania, and Luxembourg
19. The Tea Party
20. 2010

# Quiz 41: Pot Luck

EASY

1. What name is given to a triangle that has two sides of equal length?

2. What board game is known in America as checkers?

3. Who was the best-selling author in Britain in the 2000s?

4. 'Lexico' was the original name of which popular board game?

5. How many riders take part in a speedway race?

6. In relation to navigation, what do the initials GPS stand for?

7. 'Live long and prosper' is a catchphrase from which TV show?

8. 'The Untold Story of the Witches of Oz' is the subtitle of which hit West End musical?

9. Which king of Mercia built a dyke from the River Dee to the River Wye?

10. In degrees Celsius, what is the boiling point of water?

11. What is the poisonous plant belladonna also known as?

12. What bird, a member of the crow family, is also the name of a chess piece?

13. Which soul singer was known as 'The Hardest Working Man in Showbusiness'?

14. Who is Channel 4's 'Chatty Man'?

15. Bloomer, ciabatta, and French stick are types of which food?

16. Kristiania is the former name of which European capital city?

Answers – page 85

17. What do the initials RSPB stand for?

18. The largest coral reef in the world lies off the coast of which country?

19. What is the international dialling code for the United Kingdom?
    a) +44
    b) +45
    c) +46

20. 'The Lancet' is a journal primarily aimed at workers in which profession?
    a) building
    b) legal
    c) medical

## Answers to Quiz 40: Connections part 1

1. Grandad
2. Nelson Mandela
3. Albert
4. Derek and the Dominoes
5. Markets
6. Trevor Francis
7. The Trotters
8. Damien Thorn
9. Trigger
10. Mike
11. Cassandra
12. Chandelier
13. Camberwell and Peckham
14. Raquel Watts
15. Rodney Bewes
16. Marlene Dietrich
17. Mickey
18. Kat Slater
19. Max Boyce
20. The TV show 'Only Fools and Horses'

# Quiz 42: Connections part 2

1. 'Sit Down' and 'She's a Star' were top ten hits for which Manchester band?

2. What is the official office and residence of the British prime minister?

3. Whose assassination in Sarajevo in June 1914 brought about the start of the First World War?

4. 'Don't Be A Stranger', 'It's Too Late', and 'The Perfect Year' were top five hits in the 1990s for which female British singer?

5. Which British singer's only number one single was the 1983 hit 'Wherever I Lay My Hat (That's My Home)'?

6. Who was murdered by Mark Chapman in New York in 1980?

7. What was the name of the 1980s TV drama that starred Robert Wagner and Stefanie Powers as amateur detectives?

8. 'You're the First, the Last, My Everything' was the only number one hit by which soul singer?

9. Who was the original host of TV game show 'Catchphrase'?

10. What was the name of Arthur Daley's sidekick in the 1980s drama 'Minder'?

11. Who left his post as Governor of the Bank of England in June 2013?

12. Which English novelist created the fictional character Moll Flanders?

13. Which word precedes 'touch' and 'set' when spoken by a referee organizing a rugby scrum?

14. Which American singer recorded the theme tune to the hit movie 'Ghostbusters'?

15. What was the middle name of US president Lyndon Johnson?

16. Which American composer and songwriter's works include 'I've Got You Under My Skin' and 'I Get a Kick Out of You'?

17. Which St Lucian-born poet was awarded the Nobel Prize for Literature in 1992?

18. Ninian Joseph Yule Jr was the birth name of which veteran American actor who provided the voice of Tod in the animated film 'The Fox and the Hound'?

19. In a Formula One race, what colour flag represents all clear?
    a) blue
    c) green
    c) yellow

20. What is the connection between all the answers?

## Answers to Quiz 41: Pot Luck

1. Isosceles
2. Draughts
3. JK Rowling
4. Scrabble
5. Four
6. Global Positioning System
7. Star Trek
8. Wicked
9. Offa
10. 100 degrees
11. Deadly nightshade
12. Rook
13. James Brown
14. Alan Carr
15. Bread
16. Oslo
17. Royal Society for the Protection of Birds
18. Australia
19. +44
20. Medical

# Quiz 43: Pot Luck

1. 'Viva Forever!' is a musical based on the songs of which band?

2. Who was the captain of England's 2009 Ashes-winning cricket team?

3. Daniel Craig made his debut as James Bond in which film?

4. Which two-word phrase meaning a blunder comes from the French for 'false step'?

5. 'On My Own' and 'Do You Hear the People Sing?' are songs from which West End musical?

6. 'Mittwoch' is the German word for which day of the week?

7. Which British actor played Gandalf in the film trilogy 'The Lord of the Rings'?

8. Maris Piper and King Edward are popular varieties of which vegetable?

9. Cain, Abel and Seth, were the three sons of which Biblical couple?

10. Which renowned wit could 'resist anything but temptation'?

11. The flag of Spain is made up of which two colours?

12. Craig Newmark was the founder of which online classified advertising website?

13. Highbury is the former home of which English football club?

14. What was the first commercial aeroplane to fly faster than the speed of sound?

15. Bondi Beach is in which Commonwealth city?

16. Which UK political party has the initials UUP?

Answers – page 89

17. According to the proverb, you should 'hope for the best but...'

18. What ancient form of treatment uses needles to relieve pain?

19. The ECB is the governing body in England and Wales of which sport?
    a) basketball
    b) boxing
    c) cricket

20. Sergio Leone is most commonly associated with which genre of films?
    a) romantic comedies
    b) science fiction
    c) westerns

## Answers to Quiz 42: Connections part 2

1. James
2. 10 Downing Street
3. Archduke Franz Ferdinand
4. Dina Carroll
5. Paul Young
6. John Lennon
7. Hart to Hart
8. Barry White
9. Roy Walker
10. Terry McCann
11. Mervyn King
12. Daniel Defoe
13. Crouch
14. Ray Parker Junior
15. Baines
16. Cole Porter
17. Derek Walcott
18. Mickey Rooney
19. Green
20. They all feature the surname of a recent England football international

# Quiz 44: History

1. In which year did World War II end?

2. In 1980, a team of SAS personnel ended a hostage crisis after storming the London embassy of which country?

3. Which Shakespearean phrase was used to describe the period of industrial unrest in Britain in 1978 and 1979?

4. What was the name of the ship on which the Pilgrim Fathers sailed from Plymouth to America in 1620?

5. The Battle of Balaclava was fought during which conflict?

6. Who was in charge of the German Luftwaffe during World War II?

7. Which word, meaning a mounted soldier, was given to supporters of the Royalist cause in the English Civil War?

8. Which French heroine was known as the Maid of Orleans?

9. What was the name of Nelson's flagship at the Battle of Trafalgar?

10. Who was the first Roman emperor?

11. Which country undertook an industrialization programme in 1958 known as the 'Great Leap Forward'?

12. In 1945, the US dropped atomic bombs on which two Japanese cities?

13. Which European capital city gave its name to an Eastern European mutual-defence organization that operated from 1955 until 1991?

14. The Battle of Gettysburg was fought in which war?

15. What title was given to the emperor of Germany following unification in 1870?

16. The Black Death ravaged Europe in which century?

17. Who was the Chancellor of Germany from 1982 until 1998?

18. The Battle of Naseby was the most decisive battle in which conflict?

19. President John F Kennedy was assassinated in which city?
    a) Dallas
    b) New York
    c) Washington

20. The scene of major battles in World War II, El Alamein is in which country?
    a) Algeria
    b) Egypt
    c) Tunisia

## Answers to Quiz 43: Pot Luck

| | |
|---|---|
| 1. The Spice Girls | 11. Red and yellow |
| 2. Andrew Strauss | 12. Craigslist.com |
| 3. Casino Royale | 13. Arsenal |
| 4. Faux pas | 14. Concorde |
| 5. Les Miserables | 15. Sydney |
| 6. Wednesday | 16. Ulster Unionist Party |
| 7. Sir Ian McKellan | 17. Prepare for the worst |
| 8. Potato | 18. Acupuncture |
| 9. Adam and Eve | 19. Cricket |
| 10. Oscar Wilde | 20. Westerns |

# Quiz 45: Pot Luck

1. Fine Gael and Fianna Fail are political parties in which European country?

2. The musical 'Mamma Mia!' is based on the songs of which pop group?

3. Which American author said, 'It is better to keep your mouth closed and let people think you are a fool than to open it and remove all doubt'?

4. Brooklyn, Cruz, Romeo, and Harper are the children of which famous couple?

5. The Wailing Wall is a holy site in which religion?

6. Fish named Marlin and Dory are the central characters in which 2003 Pixar animation?

7. What name is given to a triangle that has three sides that are all different lengths?

8. How many colours feature on a Rubik's Cube?

9. Which sport features teams called the Kolkata Knight Riders, Delhi Daredevils, and Rajasthan Royals?

10. Which British actor played spymaster George Smiley in the 2011 film 'Tinker, Tailor, Soldier, Spy'?

11. 'Freddie' is the nickname of which England cricketer-turned-boxer?

12. The Russian flag features which three colours?

13. Maine Road was the former home of which English football club?

14. 'Dark Side of the Moon', which stayed in the charts for 741 weeks, was an album by which band?

15. In which sport can a player score a strike and a spare?

16. The musical 'West Side Story' is based on which Shakespeare play?

17. What was the surname of the fictional film boxer 'Rocky'?

18. How many contestants start each episode of the TV quiz show 'Pointless'?

19. +1 is the international dialling code for which country?
    a) USA
    b) Australia
    c) Ireland

20. Which of the following means in secret?
    a) in camera
    b) in record
    c) in cassette

## Answers to Quiz 44: History

1. 1945
2. Iran
3. Winter of Discontent
4. The Mayflower
5. The Crimean War
6. Hermann Göring
7. Cavalier
8. Joan of Arc
9. HMS Victory
10. Augustus
11. China
12. Hiroshima and Nagasaki
13. Warsaw (Pact)
14. The American Civil War
15. Kaiser
16. 14th
17. Helmut Kohl
18. The English Civil War
19. Dallas
20. Egypt

# Quiz 46: Countries that Start with a Vowel

EASY

1. The Kangaroos is the nickname of the rugby league team of which country?

2. The pyramids of Giza are in which country?

3. Boca Juniors and River Plate are major football teams in which country?

4. Dubai is a major city in which Middle Eastern country?

5. Which South American country's name derives from the Latin word for silver?

6. Record-breaking runner Haile Gebrselassie is the from which African country?

7. The Republic of Ireland shares a land border with which country?

8. What is the largest country in Africa?

9. The final of the Euro 2012 football tournament was hosted in which country?

10. Tashkent is the capital city of which landlocked former Soviet Republic?

11. 'Old Glory' is the nickname of the flag of which country?

12. Idi Amin was the long-time president of which African country?

13. 'Waltzing Matilda' is an unofficial anthem of which country?

14. Alexandria is the second largest city in which country?

15. Which country won the World Cup for the third time in 2006?

16. Graz is the second largest city in which European country?

Answers – page 95

17. The Galápagos Islands are territories under the control of which South American country?

18. Which European country has borders with Greece, Macedonia, Montenegro, and Kosovo?

19. Which East African country gained independence from Ethiopia in 1991?
    a) Angola
    b) Eritrea
    c) Uganda

20. The panama hat in fact originated not in Panama but in which country?
    a) Argentina
    b) Ecuador
    c) United States of America

## Answers to Quiz 45: Pot Luck

1. Republic of Ireland
2. Abba
3. Mark Twain
4. David and Victoria Beckham
5. Judaism
6. Finding Nemo
7. Scalene
8. Six
9. Cricket
10. Gary Oldman
11. Andrew Flintoff
12. Red, white, and blue
13. Manchester City
14. Pink Floyd
15. Ten-pin bowling
16. Romeo and Juliet
17. Balboa
18. Eight
19. USA
20. In camera

# Quiz 47: Pot Luck

1. Boyband Westlife are from which country?

2. The WBO, WBA, and IBF are governing bodies in which sport?

3. 'Mirrors' was a massive 2013 hit for which former boy-band star, singer, and actor?

4. Who provided the voice of Princess Fiona in the 'Shrek' films?

5. Who was the British prime minister from 1990 until 1997?

6. Haematology is the study of what substance?

7. Which religious leader gives a blessing at Christmas and Easter called 'Urbi et Orbi'?

8. 'Lundi' is the French word for which day of the week?

9. Which jockey was banned from horse racing for six months in December 2012 after failing a drugs test?

10. In the 'Mr Men' series, what colour is Mr Tickle?

11. Who is the current host of the TV quiz show 'Mastermind'?

12. The name of which province of Canada means 'New Scotland'?

13. What was the first name of the composer Purcell?

14. A sommelier is an expert on what type of drink?

15. 'The Whirlwind' is the nickname of which snooker player?

16. 'The Soldier's Song' is the national anthem of which country?

17. Which fruit is also the name of the oldest child of singer Chris Martin and actress Gwyneth Paltrow?

Answers – page 97

18. What does a philatelist collect?

19. Hugh Laurie rowed in the Boat Race in 1980 for which
    university?
    a) Oxford
    b) Cambridge
    c) Hull

20. What is the name of the butler in the Batman films?
    a) Albert
    b) Arthur
    c) Austin

EASY

## Answers to Quiz 46: Countries that Start with a Vowel

| | | | |
|---|---|---|---|
| 1. | Australia | 11. | United States of America |
| 2. | Egypt | 12. | Uganda |
| 3. | Argentina | 13. | Australia |
| 4. | United Arab Emirates | 14. | Egypt |
| 5. | Argentina | 15. | Italy |
| 6. | Ethiopia | 16. | Austria |
| 7. | United Kingdom | 17. | Ecuador |
| 8. | Algeria | 18. | Albania |
| 9. | Ukraine | 19. | Eritrea |
| 10. | Uzbekistan | 20. | Ecuador |

# Quiz 48: Connections part 3

1. What weapon is used to fire an arrow?

2. In addition to Dermot Murnaghan, which journalist and broadcaster has hosted the TV quiz show 'Eggheads'?

3. The 1953 novel 'Casino Royale' was the first novel to feature which fictional spy?

4. John Lennon Airport serves which city?

5. Which English county is known as the 'Garden of England'?

6. What is the name of the biggest and busiest railway station in Manchester?

7. The TV detective drama 'Endeavour' is set in which city?

8. In which English city does the football team nicknamed the Sky Blues play its home games?

9. Which historic English country borders Cumbria to the west, County Durham to the south, and the Scottish Borders to the north?

10. What is the name of the football match played at the start of the season between the previous season's league champions and FA Cup winners?

11. De Montfort University is in which English city?

12. What is the name of the ITV crime drama starring Rupert Penry-Jones and Phil Davis which originally featured a killer copying Jack the Ripper?

13. 'If you change your mind, I'm the first in line' is the opening line to which song by Abba?

14. Which word describes a person who rules during the minority, absence, or disability of a monarch?

Answers – page 99

15. Which London railway station is the southern terminus of the West Coast Mainline?

16. Which British actor and comedian plays JP in the university drama 'Fresh Meat' and Alfie Wickers in 'Bad Education'?

17. Who was the first South Korean footballer to win the Premier League?

18. Which Elvis Presley song was the first ever single to enter the UK chart at number one?

19. What is the highest rank in the Royal Navy?

20. What is the connection between all the answers?

**EASY**

## Answers to Quiz 47: Pot Luck

1. Republic of Ireland
2. Boxing
3. Justin Timberlake
4. Cameron Diaz
5. John Major
6. Blood
7. The Pope
8. Monday
9. Frankie Dettori
10. Orange
11. John Humphrys
12. Nova Scotia
13. Henry
14. Wine
15. Jimmy White
16. Republic of Ireland
17. Apple
18. Stamps
19. Cambridge
20. Albert

# Quiz 49: Pot Luck

1.  Which season is known in America as fall?

2.  Which star of 'Little Britain' is a judge on 'Britain's Got Talent'?

3.  What is the sum total of the angles of a triangle regardless of its shape?

4.  In which sport is the PGA a governing body?

5.  What girl's name is also the name of a song traditionally sung at Christmas?

6.  'Klavier' is the German word for which musical instrument?

7.  A nonet is a piece of music written for how many instruments?

8.  Which actor played Jedi knight Qui-Gon Jinn in the 'Star Wars' films?

9.  Which footballer caused controversy by biting an opponent during Liverpool's 2013 game against Chelsea at Anfield?

10. Which chemical element has the atomic number 13 and the symbol Al?

11. Which singer released the 1990 compilation album 'The Immaculate Collection'?

12. What is Britain's best-selling Sunday newspaper?

13. If all the teams in cricket's County Championship were listed alphabetically, which would be at the bottom of the list?

14. Nooglers is a nickname given to new employees of which company?

15. Which actor is known as 'The Muscles from Brussels'?

EASY

16. Dermatology is the scientific study of which part of the human body?

17. Freddy Krueger is a central character in which series of horror films?

18. The Imola motor-racing circuit is in which country?

19. Which English football team plays its home games at the DW Stadium?
    a) Derby County
    b) Watford
    c) Wigan Athletic

20. Which food, popular with climbers, takes its name from a town in Cumbria?
    a) Carlisle mint cake
    b) Kendal mint cake
    c) Whitehaven mint cake

## Answers to Quiz 48: Connections part 3

1. Bow
2. Jeremy Vine
3. James Bond
4. Liverpool
5. Kent
6. Piccadilly
7. Oxford
8. Coventry
9. Northumberland
10. Community Shield
11. Leicester
12. Whitechapel
13. Take a Chance on Me
14. Regent
15. Euston
16. Jack Whitehall
17. Park Ji-Sung
18. Jailhouse Rock
19. Admiral of the Fleet
20. The answers all feature a square on the standard Monopoly board

# Quiz 50: Connections part 4

1.  Which actor starred in the films 'Drive', 'The Ides of March', and 'Half Nelson'?

2.  'Hotel California' was which band's only UK top ten hit?

3.  What term is used to describe a score of three under par on a golf hole?

4.  Which nurse was also known as 'The Lady with the Lamp'?

5.  Which car manufacturer produces the XF, XJ and F-Type models?

6.  What is the nickname of the Australian rugby union team?

7.  Which 16th-century English sailor circumnavigated the globe in a ship called 'The Golden Hind'?

8.  Castle is another name for which chess piece?

9.  Which Norwich-based broadcaster is the alter ego of Steve Coogan?

10. Sir Anthony Hopkins won a Best Actor Oscar in 1991 for his performance in which thriller?

11. What is the nickname of Norwich City Football Club?

12. In 'The Wizard of Oz', which character lacked courage?

13. Which American singer sang the theme tune to the James Bond film 'Tomorrow Never Dies'?

14. 'Crazy' and 'Kiss from a Rose' were the biggest hits by which British singer?

15. Complete the title of the 2008 film featuring the voices of Jack Black and Angelina Jolie: 'Kung Fu ...'

Answers – page 103

16. Penfold was the sidekick of which animated superhero?

17. Who is the General Secretary of the National Union of Rail, Maritime, and Transport Workers (RMT)?

18. What is the nickname of Watford FC?
    a) The Bees
    b) The Hornets
    c) The Wasps

19. What was the nickname of the German military leader Erwin Rommel?
    a) The Desert Fox
    b) The Desert Hound
    c) The Desert Rat

20. What is the connection between the answers?

## Answers to Quiz 49: Pot Luck

1. Autumn
2. David Walliams
3. 180
4. Golf
5. Carol
6. Piano
7. Nine
8. Liam Neeson
9. Luis Suarez
10. Aluminium
11. Madonna
12. The Sun on Sunday
13. Yorkshire
14. Google
15. Jean-Claude Van Damme
16. Skin
17. A Nightmare on Elm Street
18. San Marino
19. Wigan Athletic
20. Kendal mint cake

# Quiz 51: Pot Luck

EASY

1. In which gallery can you see the famous painting 'Mona Lisa'?

2. Donnelly and McPartlin are the surnames of which comedy double act?

3. Which word describes the distance from the centre of a circle to the perimeter?

4. Which female singer has had the most UK number one singles?

5. What is the only capital city of a European Union country that starts with the letter C?

6. Which popular dessert takes its name from the French for 'burnt cream'?

7. Which branch of science takes its name from the Greek for 'study of life'?

8. What is the main ingredient in the Mexican dip guacamole?

9. Brass is an alloy of zinc and which other metal?

10. What was the name of the artificial language created by Ludwig Zamenhof?

11. Which brand of soft drink is also the name of an Argentine dance?

12. What is the square root of 169?

13. The apple brandy Calvados comes from which country?

14. Which river flows through Durham to the North Sea at Sunderland?

15. Which businessman was the founder of the News International empire?

Answers – page 105

16. Telford is the largest town in which English county?

17. Salvador Dali, Rene Magritte, and Max Ernst are associated with which artistic movement?

18. Which Irish actor played The Scarecrow in 'Batman Begins' and 'The Dark Knight'?

19. Lady Godiva rode naked through which city?
    a) Coventry
    b) Leicester
    c) Nottingham

20. What name is given to an angle that is smaller than 90 degrees?
    a) acute
    b) obtuse
    c) right

**EASY**

## Answers to Quiz 50: Connections part 4

1. Ryan Gosling
2. Eagles
3. Albatross
4. Florence Nightingale
5. Jaguar
6. The Wallabies
7. Sir Francis Drake
8. Rook
9. Alan Partridge
10. The Silence of the Lambs
11. The Canaries
12. The Lion
13. Sheryl Crow
14. Seal
15. Panda
16. Danger Mouse
17. Bob Crow
18. The Hornets
19. The Desert Fox
20. They all contain the name of an animal

# Quiz 52: Slogans

Identify the company associated with the slogans below:

1. 'They're gr-r-r-reat'

2. 'Don't leave home without it'

3. 'Finger lickin' good'

4. 'Snap! Crackle! Pop!'

5. 'Reassuringly expensive'

6. 'The ultimate driving machine'

7. 'Mum's gone to ...'

8. 'Good things come to those who wait'

9. 'How do you eat yours?'

10. 'Don't be evil'

11. 'Have it your way'

12. 'Quality never goes out of fashion'

13. 'Saving you money every day'

14. 'Always giving you extra'

15. 'The best a man can get'

16. 'The power of dreams'

17. 'Loves the jobs you hate'

18. 'Kills all known germs dead'

19. 'Motion and emotion'

20. 'Ideas for life'

## Answers to Quiz 51: Pot Luck

1. The Louvre
2. Ant and Dec
3. Radius
4. Madonna
5. Copenhagen
6. Crème brûlée
7. Biology
8. Avocado
9. Copper
10. Esperanto
11. Tango
12. 13
13. France
14. River Wear
15. Rupert Murdoch
16. Shropshire
17. Surrealism
18. Cillian Murphy
19. Coventry
20. Acute

# Quiz 53: Pot Luck

1. What type of pasta means 'little tubes' in Italian?

2. What are the two European Union capitals that start with the letter R?

3. Pretoria is the administrative capital of which country?

4. Which bird appears on the coat of arms of Australia?

5. Sydney is the largest city in which Australian state?

6. Magyar is an alternative name for which European language?

7. Which metallic element, first isolated by Humphrey Davy, has the atomic number 12 and the chemical symbol Mg?

8. Which letter lies between H and K on a standard computer keyboard?

9. What is the highest rank in the British Army?

10. In publishing, what do the initials ISBN stand for?

11. In the human body, what are incisors, canines, molars, and premolars?

12. Which actor played Andy Dalziel in the police drama 'Dalziel and Pascoe'?

13. What is the sweet syrup formed by bees from the nectar of flowers?

14. In Britain it's called a car bonnet. What is it called in America?

15. Hydropathy is a method of treating disease with what substance?

Answers – page 109

16. Which central London thoroughfare was noted for journalism and the press?

17. Of what is horology the scientific study?

18. What is the title given to the official reports of UK parliamentary debates?

19. What name describes a period of fine sunny weather during autumn?
    a) Arabic summer
    b) Chinese summer
    c) Indian summer

20. Which organization was founded in 1945 to promote Arab unity?
    a) Arab Community
    b) Arab League
    c) Arab Union

EASY

## Answers to Quiz 52: Slogans

1. Frosties
2. American Express
3. Kentucky Fried Chicken
4. Rice Krispies
5. Stella Artois
6. BMW
7. Iceland
8. Guinness
9. Cadbury's Creme Egg
10. Google
11. Burger King
12. Levi's
13. Asda
14. Halifax
15. Gillette
16. Honda
17. Mr Muscle
18. Domestos
19. Peugeot
20. Panasonic

# Quiz 54: Love and Marriage

1.   Which metal is traditionally associated with a 50th wedding anniversary?

2.   Which famous couple tied the knot on 29 April 2011?

3.   Which member of Girls Aloud topped the charts in 2009 with 'Fight for This Love'?

4.   Who was the ancient Greek god of love?

5.   'There's nothing you can do that can't be done / Nothing you can sing that can't be sung / Nothing you can say but you can learn how to play the game / It's easy' are lines from which song by The Beatles?

6.   Which song by the Bee Gees provided Take That with a number one single in 1996?

7.   Who was the subject of the 1993 film biopic 'What's Love Got to Do with It'?

8.   The 1993 hit 'Mr Loverman' was the only top five single by which reggae artist?

9.   Which British singer-songwriter topped the charts in 2003 with 'Are You Ready For Love'?

10.  'Love means never having to say you're sorry' was the tagline to which 1970 film starring Ali MacGraw and Ryan O'Neal?

11.  In 1993, which American rocker would 'Do Anything For Love (But I Won't Do That)'?

12.  Which British crooner sang the theme song to the James Bond film 'From Russia With Love'?

13.  After how many years is a diamond wedding anniversary celebrated?

14.  What was the only UK number one hit single for Soft Cell?

15. Ray Romano played the title character in which long-running US sitcom?

16. 'Baby Love' and 'Where Did Our Love Go?' were hits for which Motown band?

17. Who topped the charts in 1988 with 'A Groovy Kind of Love'?

18. Courtney Michelle Harrison is the real name of which actress and singer who was married to an iconic rock star who died in 1993?

19. What type of car was the central character in the classic children's film 'The Love Bug'?
a) Ford Capri  b) Reliant Robin  c) Volkswagen Beetle

20. According to a 1995 number one single by Eric Clapton, Cher, Chrissie Hynde, and Neneh Cherry, 'Love Can Build a ...'?
a) Bridge  b) Fence  c) Tower

## Answers to Quiz 53: Pot Luck

1. Cannelloni
2. Riga and Rome
3. South Africa
4. Emu
5. New South Wales
6. Hungarian
7. Magnesium
8. J
9. Field-Marshall
10. International Standard Book Number
11. Teeth
12. Warren Clarke
13. Honey
14. Hood
15. Water
16. Fleet Street
17. Time-measurement, including clocks
18. Hansard
19. Indian summer
20. Arab League

# Quiz 55: Pot Luck

EASY

1. Bob Cratchit and Tiny Tim are characters in which story by Charles Dickens?

2. Which three-leaved plant is the national emblem of Ireland?

3. Dean Cain, George Reeves, and Brandon Routh have all played which superhero?

4. Which nautical term refers to the right-hand side of a ship?

5. What is the name of the chain of beads used by Catholics when reciting and counting prayers?

6. 'The Iliad' and 'The Odyssey' were written by which ancient Greek poet?

7. In internet slang, what do the initials LOL stand for?

8. Which Hollywood superstar, who died in 2008, played Scott Irwin in the TV soap 'Home and Away'?

9. A niqab is a face veil worn by some followers of which religion?

10. Which American state capital was named after a 19th-century German leader?

11. Quicksilver is an alternative name for which chemical element?

12. 'We Have All the Time in the World' by Louis Armstrong features heavily in which James Bond film?

13. Which imperial measure is equal to 6.35kg?

14. Which spirit is mixed with orange juice to make the cocktail known as a Screwdriver?

15. Which unit of length is also the word used to describe the rhythmical pattern of a poem?

16. Albert Finney, Peter Ustinov, and David Suchet have all played which dapper detective?

17. An internet domain ending with the letters .es is from which country?

18. Founded by Earl Haig in 1921, which ex-servicemen's welfare organization is responsible for the annual Remembrance Day poppy appeal?

19. In the 'Mr Men' series, what colour is Mr Forgetful?
    a) Blue
    b) Green
    c) Red

20. How many letters are there on the bottom row of a standard computer keyboard?
    a) six
    b) seven
    c) eight

## Answers to Quiz 54: Love and Marriage

1.  Gold
2.  Prince William and Kate Middleton
3.  Cheryl Cole
4.  Eros
5.  All You Need Is Love
6.  How Deep Is Your Love
7.  Tina Turner
8.  Shabba Ranks
9.  Elton John
10. Love Story
11. Meat Loaf
12. Matt Monro
13. 60
14. Tainted Love
15. Everybody Loves Raymond
16. The Supremes
17. Phil Collins
18. Courtney Love
19. Volkswagen Beetle
20. Bridge

1. Which heavyweight boxing champion was the first man to win the BBC Sports Personality of the Year award more than once?

2. What is the golf club known as a 1 wood also called?

3. In 2011, Matt Smith became the eleventh incarnation of which TV character?

4. What is the animated character Patrick Clifton better known as?

5. Which word is used to describe a trial episode made for a proposed television series?

6. Which fictional detective, who was played by Angela Lansbury, lived in Cabot Cove?

7. Which animated TV programme is set in the fictional Welsh town of Pontypandy?

8. Bronze is an alloy that consists of tin and which other metal?

9. Which Singapore-born footballer, who appeared for Ipswich, Rangers, Coventry, and Sunderland, won 77 caps for England and played in three World Cups?

10. 'You Make Me Wanna', 'Yeah', and 'Burn' were UK number ones for which American R&B star?

11. Who was elected for a second term as prime minister in 1983?

12. Which actor succeeded Peter Davison as TV's 'Dr Who'?

13. Who topped the charts in 2000 with 'Can We Fix It?' and in 2001 with a cover of 'Mambo No. 5'?

14. What was the name of the character played by Matthew Perry in 'Friends'?

15. 'Yesterday Once More' and '(They Long To Be) Close To You' were top ten hits for which band?

16. What Bob Marley and the Wailers song reached number 4 in the UK singles chart in May 1983?

17. Which silent film won the Oscar for Best Film in 2012?

18. What was the title of a 2001 hit single by the Stereophonics?
    a) Mr Reader
    b) Mr Sailor
    c) Mr Writer

19. What was the name of a 2000 film comedy starring Renee Zellweger, Morgan Freeman, and Chris Rock?
    a) Nurse Betty
    b) Nurse Lizzy
    c) Nurse Wendy

20. What is the connection between the answers?

## Answers to Quiz 55: Pot Luck

1. A Christmas Carol
2. Shamrock
3. Superman
4. Starboard
5. Rosary beads
6. Homer
7. Laugh out loud
8. Heath Ledger
9. Islam
10. Bismarck
11. Mercury
12. On Her Majesty's Secret Service
13. A stone
14. Vodka
15. Metre
16. Hercule Poirot
17. Spain
18. The Royal British Legion
19. Blue
20. Seven

# Quiz 57: Pot Luck

EASY

1. Which two dances represent letters in the NATO Phonetic Alphabet?

2. What is the only capital city of a European Union country that starts with the letter N?

3. Which international sporting organization has the initials IOC?

4. According to the proverb, what is worth a thousand words?

5. What is the name of the victim in the board game Cluedo?

6. On a London Underground map, what colour is the Central line?

7. Which European city is known as the 'Queen of the Adriatic'?

8. Which word connects a hit song by Manchester rockers Oasis and a stellar explosion that occurs when white dwarf stars collide?

9. Georgetown is the capital city of which South American country?

10. The Talmud is a sacred text in which religion?

11. Which US state capital was named after an English explorer, adventurer, and writer who died in 1618?

12. Which of the Brontë sisters wrote 'The Tenant of Wildfell Hall'?

13. Margaret Rutherford and Joan Hickson both played which literary sleuth?

14. Who is the only female judge on the TV talent show 'The Voice'?

15. The IRB is the global governing body for which sport?

16. 'I Dreamed a Dream' is a song from which stage musical?

17. In which sport do teams compete for the Calcutta Cup?

18. Who was the first team to win the top flight of English football 20 times?

19. In a game of chess, each player starts with how many pawns?
    a) two
    b) four
    c) eight

20. What is the name of the children's TV character played by Justin Fletcher?
    a) Mr Bumble
    b) Mr Mumble
    c) Mr Tumble

**EASY**

## Answers to Quiz 56: Connections part 5

1. Henry Cooper
2. A driver
3. Dr Who
4. Postman Pat
5. Pilot
6. Jessica Fletcher
7. Fireman Sam
8. Copper
9. Terry Butcher
10. Usher
11. Margaret Thatcher
12. Colin Baker
13. Bob the Builder
14. Chandler Bing
15. The Carpenters
16. Buffalo Soldier
17. The Artist
18. Mr Writer
19. Nurse Betty
20. They all contain an occupation or job

# Quiz 58: Anagrams of Football Teams

Rearrange the letters to make the names of top British and European football clubs:

1. Love or lip

2. Nag errs

3. Red admiral

4. Earl bacon

5. Ran sale

6. Veer not

7. Can mail

8. Sea lech

9. Urban chimney

10. Ham flu

11. Whines mutated

12. A decent miser hunt

13. Stretchy iceman

14. Vital salon

EASY

15. Mutant hoops

16. Acne fib

17. Larded nuns

18. I throw cynic

19. Sudden elite

20. Thermostat hot pun

## Answers to Quiz 57. Pot Luck

1. Foxtrot and Tango
2. Nicosia
3. International Olympic Committee
4. A picture
5. Dr Black
6. Red
7. Venice
8. (Champagne) Supernova
9. Guyana
10. Judaism
11. Raleigh (after Sir Walter Raleigh)
12. Anne Brontë
13. Miss Marple
14. Jessie J
15. Rugby union
16. Les Miserables
17. Rugby union
18. Manchester United
19. Eight
20. Mr Tumble

# Quiz 59: Pot Luck

1. Which South American capital city represents a letter in the NATO Phonetic Alphabet?

2. What are the five European Union capitals that start with the letter B?

3. In snooker, which ball is worth more, the green or the brown?

4. Mama Morton, Billy Flynn, and Roxie Hart are characters in which stage musical?

5. Who was the first SNP politician to hold the post of First Minister of Scotland?

6. Which word is a slang term for a journalist and a term for illegally breaking into a computer system?

7. The dish hotpot is most commonly associated with which English county?

8. Which dinosaur's name is the Latin for 'king of the tyrant lizards'?

9. A Capetonian is the name given to a person from which African city?

10. On a standard computer keyboard, which letter sits between B and M?

11. The IAAF is the international governing body for which sport?

12. 'For anyone who has ever wished upon a star' was the tagline of which 1940 animated Disney classic?

13. Majorca, Menorca, Ibiza, and Formentera are part of which island group?

14. Which country made its Test cricket debut in November 2000?

EASY

15. In Roman numerals, which number is represented by the letter M?

16. 'Luck Be a Lady' and 'Sit Down, You're Rockin' the Boat' are songs from which hit musical?

17. How many players are in a cricket team?

18. Goa and Karnataka are states of which country?

19. How many stars appear on the flag of New Zealand?
    a) four
    b) five
    c) six

20. Which French name is the capital city of the US state of South Dakota?
    a) François
    b) Nicolas
    c) Pierre

## Answers to Quiz 58: Anagrams of Football Teams

| | | | |
|---|---|---|---|
| 1. | Liverpool | 11. | West Ham United |
| 2. | Rangers | 12. | Manchester United |
| 3. | Real Madrid | 13. | Manchester City |
| 4. | Barcelona | 14. | Aston Villa |
| 5. | Arsenal | 15. | Southampton |
| 6. | Everton | 16. | Benfica |
| 7. | AC Milan | 17. | Sunderland |
| 8. | Chelsea | 18. | Norwich City |
| 9. | Bayern Munich | 19. | Leeds United |
| 10. | Fulham | 20. | Tottenham Hotspur |

# Quiz 60: Places

EASY

1. Peking is the former name of which Asian city?

2. Nippon is the official name of which country?

3. Murrayfield Stadium can be found in which British city?

4. What is the largest city in the US state of Illinois?

5. In which county will you see the ancient monument Stonehenge?

6. Headingley cricket ground is in which English city?

7. What is the UK's busiest passenger seaport?

8. Aintree racecourse is in which English city?

9. The TV sitcoms 'Only Fools and Horses' and 'Desmond's' were set in which London district?

10. What name is shared by the capital of Western Australia and a city in Scotland situated on the River Tay?

11. Home of the famous Cadbury factory, Bournville is a suburb of which English city?

12. Windermere and Coniston Water are features of which UK National Park?

13. A Cantabrigian is someone from which city?

14. Tampere, Turku, and Oulu are cities in which European country?

15. In terms of population, what is the largest Spanish-speaking country in the world?

16. Schoenefeld and Tegel are airports that serve which European capital?

Answers – page 123

17. The name of which American city translates into English as 'the meadows'?

18. Hallam, Heeley, Brightside, and Hillsborough are parliamentary constituencies in which British city?

19. Which country in Africa has the largest population?
    a) Algeria
    b) Egypt
    c) Nigeria

20. The Seychelles are located in which ocean?
    a) Atlantic
    b) Indian
    c) Pacific

## Answers to Quiz 59: Pot Luck

1. Lima
2. Berlin, Bratislava, Brussels, Bucharest, Budapest
3. Brown
4. Chicago
5. Alex Salmond
6. Hack
7. Lancashire
8. Tyrannosaurus rex
9. Cape Town
10. N
11. Athletics
12. Pinocchio
13. The Balearics
14. Bangladesh
15. 1000
16. Guys and Dolls
17. 11
18. India
19. Four
20. Pierre

# Quiz 61: Pot Luck

1.  Which sport represents a letter in the NATO Phonetic Alphabet?

2.  Complete the title of the 1933 book by George Orwell: 'Down and Out in Paris and ...'

3.  Who was the Russian prime minister from 2008 until 2012?

4.  Tony McCoy and Barry Geraghty are notable names in which sport?

5.  'Swan Lake', 'The Sleeping Beauty', and 'The Nutcracker' are ballets from which Russian composer?

6.  What is the medical name for the voice box?

7.  What was the currency of Spain before the adoption of the euro?

8.  Persia is the former name of which country in the Middle East?

9.  'Nabucco' and 'Aida' are operas by which Italian composer?

10. The Azores are an autonomous region of which European country?

11. What does the N in the acronym NATO stand for?

12. Which South African clergyman was awarded the Nobel Peace Prize in 1984?

13. Melbourne is the largest city in which Australian state?

14. The PDC and the BDO are governing bodies in which indoor sport?

15. Which American author wrote 'A Connecticut Yankee in King Arthur's Court'?

16. What is a myocardial infarction more commonly known as?

17. Which workers' organization has the initials TUC?

18. The Blockheads were the backing band for which singer who died in 2000?

19. What was the first name of the British composer Vaughan Williams?
    a) Ralph
    b) Richard
    c) Robert

20. Before becoming manager of Manchester United, Sir Alex Ferguson was boss of which Scottish club?
    a) Aberdeen
    b) Dundee United
    c) Hearts

## Answers to Quiz 60: Places

1. Beijing
2. Japan
3. Edinburgh
4. Chicago
5. Wiltshire
6. Leeds
7. Dover
8. Liverpool
9. Peckham
10. Perth
11. Birmingham
12. The Lake District
13. Cambridge
14. Finland
15. Mexico
16. Berlin
17. Las Vegas
18. Sheffield
19. Nigeria
20. Indian

# Quiz 62: Sport part 2

1.  Which country did England beat to win the 2003 Rugby World Cup final?

2.  Who kicked the drop goal that sealed that win for England?

3.  Who are the two German drivers to have won the Formula One Drivers' Championship?

4.  The Warriors are a rugby league team from which town?

5.  Whom did Andre Villas Boas succeed as manager of Tottenham Hotspur?

6.  Which flag is waved at the end of a Formula One race?

7.  Who captained England to victory in the 2010/11 Ashes series in Australia?

8.  After six years in charge, Tony Pulis left his job as manager of which football club in May 2013?

9.  Craven Cottage is the home ground of which English football team?

10. Which is longer – a snooker table or a table-tennis table?

11. What is the only grand slam tennis tournament that is played on clay?

12. Which country eliminated England on penalties from the 2012 European Football Championships?

13. The Green Jacket is awarded to the winner of which golf tournament?

14. What nationality are boxing's Klitschko brothers?

15. Whom did Brendan Rodgers succeed as manager of Liverpool?

Answers – page 127

16. Which nickname is shared by a rugby union team in Leicester and a rugby league team in Castleford?

17. Whom did Andy Murray beat to win the US Open in 2012?

18. What is the only country to win the Cricket World Cup final on home soil?

19. The opening race of the 2013 Formula One season took place in which country?
    a) Australia
    b) Britain
    c) USA

20. Which country won its third Six Nations Championship Grand Slam in eight years in 2012?
    a) England
    b) France
    c) Wales

## Answers to Quiz 61: Pot Luck

1. Golf
2. London
3. Vladimir Putin
4. Horse racing
5. Tchaikovsky
6. Larynx
7. Peseta
8. Iran
9. Giuseppe Verdi
10. Portugal
11. North
12. Archbishop Desmond Tutu
13. Victoria
14. Darts
15. Mark Twain
16. A heart attack
17. The Trades Union Congress
18. Ian Dury
19. Ralph
20. Aberdeen

# Quiz 63: Pot Luck

1. What is alopecia more commonly known as?

2. In the Bible, who owned a coat of many colours?

3. Which animal is known as the 'ship of the desert'?

4. In 2003, which Hollywood star was elected governor of the US state of California?

5. Which Austrian psychiatrist coined the term psychoanalysis?

6. Becher's Brook and The Chair are fences at which racecourse?

7. Detective drama 'Lewis' is set in which city?

8. Which French educationalist created a system of reading and writing for blind people?

9. The resort of Sharm el-Sheikh is in which country?

10. On which two days of the week is the Euromillions lottery drawn?

11. Which TV talent show judge's autobiography is called 'Better Late Than Never: From Barrow Boy to Ballroom'?

12. According to the proverb, a watched pot never ...?

13. Which composer's works include 'Messiah', 'Water Music', and 'Music for the Royal Fireworks'?

14. Which South African won the 2012 Open Golf Championship?

15. Pop superstar Kylie Minogue first found fame in which TV soap?

16. Which Canadian province features in the NATO Phonetic Alphabet?

Answers – page 129

17. What are the two capital cities of European Union countries that start with the letter S?

18. By what name was Russian revolutionary Vladimir Ilyich Ulyanov better known?

19. Which West Indian was the first cricketer to score 400 in a Test match innings?
    a) Brian Lara
    b) Viv Richards
    c) Garfield Sobers

20. Which country did England beat to win their only football World Cup?
    a) Brazil
    b) Italy
    c) West Germany

## Answers to Quiz 62: Sport part 2

1. Australia
2. Jonny Wilkinson
3. Michael Schumacher and Sebastian Vettel
4. Wigan
5. Harry Redknapp
6. Chequered flag
7. Andrew Strauss
8. Stoke City
9. Fulham
10. Snooker table
11. French Open
12. Italy
13. The US Masters
14. Ukrainian
15. Kenny Dalglish
16. Tigers
17. Novak Djokovic
18. India
19. Australia
20. Wales

# Quiz 64: Number Two Hits

The following songs all reached number two in the UK singles chart. Simply name the artist who recorded the song.

1.  We Are the Champions (1977)

2.  Vienna (1981)

3.  Bitter Sweet Symphony (1997)

4.  Take On Me (1985)

5.  God Save the Queen (1977)

6.  Common People (1995)

7.  Rolling in the Deep (2011)

8.  The Jean Genie (1970)

9.  My Generation (1965)

10. Ray of Light (1998)

11. American Pie (1972)

12. Don't Worry Be Happy (1988)

13. Waterloo Sunset (1967)

14. Teenage Dirtbag (2001)

15. A Design for Life (1996)

Answers – page 131

16. Ride a White Swan (1970)

17. Rule the World (2007)

18. In for the Kill (2009)

19. Brianstorm (2007)

20. Put Your Records On (2006)

EASY

## Answers to Quiz 63: Pot Luck

1. Baldness
2. Joseph
3. Camel
4. Arnold Schwarzenegger
5. Sigmund Freud
6. Aintree
7. Oxford
8. Louis Braille
9. Egypt
10. Tuesday and Friday
11. Len Goodman
12. Boils
13. George Frideric Handel
14. Ernie Els
15. Neighbours
16. Quebec
17. Sofia and Stockholm
18. Lenin
19. Brian Lara
20. West Germany

# Quiz 65: Pot Luck

EASY

1. In the Bible, Jesus was betrayed in which garden?

2. What is the process of extracting gas by hydraulic fracturing more commonly known as?

3. If someone is travelling via Shanks's pony, how are they moving?

4. Scouser Craig Phillips was the first winner of which reality TV show?

5. Which celebration takes place annually on 17 March?

6. 'Cebolla' is the Spanish word for which vegetable?

7. Erdington, Kings Norton, and Handsworth are areas of which British city?

8. In relation to African politics, for what do the initials ANC stand?

9. Which superhero featured in the 2013 film 'Man of Steel'?

10. Which fictional detective features in the novel 'The Sign of the Four'?

11. What was the first name of the Polish composer Chopin?

12. Which rank in the police force is also the name of an English landscape painter born in 1776?

13. What is the name of the wife of prime minister David Cameron?

14. In 'The Simpsons', what was the name of Ned Flanders' late wife?

15. Who collaborated with Karl Marx to write the Communist Manifesto?

Answers – page 133

16. In 2009 Roger Federer became the world's most successful tennis player after winning his 16th grand slam title. Whose record did he beat?

17. Which Scottish writer wrote the children's classic 'The Wind in the Willows'?

18. Which actress was the mistress of King Charles II?

19. Which of the following is not a weapon in the board game Cluedo?
a) dagger
b) hammer
c) lead pipe

20. In which year did England last reach the semi-final of football's World Cup?
a) 1990
b) 1994
c) 1998

## Answers to Quiz 64: Number Two Hits

1. Queen
2. Ultravox
3. The Verve
4. A-Ha
5. The Sex Pistols
6. Pulp
7. Adele
8. David Bowie
9. The Who
10. Madonna
11. Don McLean
12. Bobby McFerrin
13. The Kinks
14. Wheatus
15. Manic Street Preachers
16. T Rex
17. Take That
18. La Roux
19. Arctic Monkeys
20. Corinne Bailey Rae

# Quiz 66: Name the Year

Identify the year that the following events happened:

1. England won football's World Cup.

2. The First World War ended.

3. David Cameron became prime minister.

4. London hosted the Olympic Games for the first time.

5. Neil Armstrong became the first man to walk on the moon.

6. Classic sci-fi film 'Avatar' was released.

7. Diana, Princess of Wales died in a Paris car crash.

8. Planes crashed into the Twin Towers, New York, killing thousands.

9. Manchester United completed a Premier League, FA Cup, and Champions League treble.

10. The Beatles released 'Sergeant Pepper's Lonely Hearts Club Band'.

11. The United Kingdom joined the European Economic Community.

12. The Berlin Wall fell.

13. The Magna Carta was sealed.

14. Gordon Brown succeeded Tony Blair as prime minister.

15. The Falklands War was fought between Argentina and Britain.

16. Osama bin Laden was killed.

17. Celtic became the first British club to win football's European Cup.

18. Queen Victoria was born.

19. Edward VIII abdicated from the British throne.

20. Take That topped the charts for the first time with 'Pray'.

EASY

## Answers to Quiz 65: Pot Luck

1. The Garden of Gethsemane
2. Fracking
3. On foot
4. Big Brother
5. St Patrick's Day
6. Onion
7. Birmingham
8. African National Congress
9. Superman
10. Sherlock Holmes
11. Frederic
12. Constable
13. Samantha
14. Maude
15. Friedrich Engels
16. Pete Sampras
17. Kenneth Grahame
18. Nell Gwyn
19. Hammer
20. 1990

# MEDIUM QUIZZES

# Quiz 67: Pot Luck

MEDIUM

1. Keith Lemon is the alter ego of which English comedian?

2. Who said, 'It is only shallow people who do not judge by appearances'?

3. Darts champions Phil Taylor and Adrian Lewis are from which English city?

4. Wikileaks founder Julian Assange took refuge in the London embassy of which country?

5. OFGEM is the regulator for which industries?

6. Which branch of the armed forces has museums at Hendon and Cosford?

7. What is the only London borough that begins with the letter I?

8. Who was the first female Director General of the Security Service?

9. Which word describes the representation of three-dimensional objects on a flat surface?

10. Hugo Chavez, who died in 2013, was the president of which South American country?

11. 12 Downing Street is the official residence of the holder of which political office?

12. The Cambridgeshire meeting takes place at which English racecourse?

13. True or false – the salary of the prime minister of Kenya is higher that the salary of the president of the USA?

14. The Great North Run starts in which city?

15. Which poet wrote 'The Charge of the Light Brigade'?

16. Point guard, power forward, and shooting guard are positions in which sport?

17. 'Dr Faustus', 'The Jew of Malta', and 'Tamburlaine' are works by which Elizabethan playwright?

18. In which decade was BBC 2 launched?

19. In which year was the Battle of Britain fought?
    a) 1939
    b) 1940
    c) 1941

20. 10 February 2013 was the start of the Chinese Year of the ...?
    a) Rabbit
    b) Rat
    c) Snake

## Answers to Quiz 133: Pot Luck

1. Plymouth
2. Boogie Nights
3. Iris of the eye
4. Skin
5. Berlin
6. Loose Women
7. St Petersburg
8. Close Encounters of the Third Kind
9. Moscow
10. Human immunodeficiency virus
11. The Rocky Horror Show
12. The Only Way Is Essex
13. Iceland
14. Hampshire
15. Vitali Klitschko
16. Keith Richards
17. Golf
18. Heart of Midlothian
19. Seven
20. Pastry

MEDIUM

# Quiz 68: Australia

1. Australia sits between which two oceans?

2. What is Australia's most populous state?

3. The Australian Open Tennis Championship is hosted in which city?

4. In which month is Australia Day celebrated?

5. Hobart is the capital of which Australian state?

6. What is Australia's third largest city behind Sydney and Melbourne?

7. Kingsford Smith Airport serves which Australian city?

8. Which Aussie actor played speech therapist Lionel Logue in the film 'The King's Speech'?

9. What is the Aboriginal name for Ayers Rock?

10. The capital of which state was named after the queen consort to King William IV?

11. Who was the first Australian actress to win an Oscar?

12. In 2002, who became the last Australian to win the men's singles at Wimbledon?

13. The WACA is a cricket ground in which city?

14. Australia is divided into six states and two territories. What are the two territories?

15. Which Australian novelist won the Booker Prize in 1988 and 2001 for 'Oscar and Lucinda' and 'True History of the Kelly Gang'?

16. Who was Australia's first female prime minister?

Answers – page 141

17. Which constellation appears on the Australian flag?

18. What is the smallest of Australia's mainland states by area?

19. The Brownlow Medal is awarded to the best Australian performer of the year in which sport?
    a) Australian rules football
    b) cricket
    c) rugby league

20. To the nearest million, what is the population of Australia?
    a) 17m
    b) 22m
    c) 27m

## Answers to Quiz 67: Pot Luck

1. Leigh Francis
2. Oscar Wilde
3. Stoke-on-Trent
4. Ecuador
5. Gas and electricity
6. The RAF
7. Islington
8. Dame Stella Rimington
9. Perspective
10. Venezuela
11. Government Chief Whip (Parliamentary Secretary to the Treasury)
12. Newmarket
13. True
14. Newcastle upon Tyne
15. Alfred, Lord Tennyson
16. Basketball
17. Christopher Marlowe
18. 1960s
19. 1940
20. Snake

# Quiz 69: Pot Luck

1. Which retailer coined the phrase 'The customer is always right'?

2. TV sitcom 'Citizen Khan' is set in which British city?

3. Brad Pitt played Tyler Durden in which film?

4. Which word that describes a clay water mixture used in pottery is also a fielding position in cricket?

5. Brahmin are priests in which religion?

6. Which sport would you see at Bisley?

7. What nationality was the philosopher Kierkegaard?

8. Places called Portland are the largest cities in which two US states?

9. Which military and political leader, born in the 12th century, said, 'Conquering the world on horseback is easy; it is dismounting and governing that is hard'?

10. What is the only national BBC radio station that broadcasts on Long Wave?

11. Napoleon Bonaparte died in exile on which South Atlantic island?

12. What nationality was the sculptor Rodin?

13. Which twinkle-toed Lib Dem politician appeared on the 'Strictly Come Dancing' Christmas special in 2010?

14. Yasmina Siadatan, Stella English, and Kate Walsh have all won which reality TV show?

15. Which veteran Welsh singer represented the UK at the 2013 Eurovision Song Contest?

16. What do the initials ABTA stand for?

17. What is the longest river in the British Isles?

18. Football club Juventus is based in which Italian city?

19. According to a poem by TS Eliot, what is the cruellest month?
    a) January
    b) April
    c) November

20. Which British animator, who died in 2012, created 'Thunderbirds', 'Stingray', and 'Captain Scarlet'?

MEDIUM

## Answers to Quiz 68: Australia

1. Indian and Pacific
2. New South Wales
3. Melbourne
4. January
5. Tasmania
6. Brisbane
7. Sydney
8. Geoffrey Rush
9. Uluru
10. South Australia (Adelaide)
11. Nicole Kidman
12. Lleyton Hewitt
13. Perth
14. Australian Capital Territory and Northern Territory
15. Peter Carey
16. Julia Gillard
17. Southern Cross
18. Victoria
19. Australian rules football
20. 22m

# Quiz 70: Books

1. The 2012 novel 'The Casual Vacancy' was the first adult book by which best-selling author?

2. Which famous detective is the central character in Anthony Horowitz's 2011 novel 'The House of Silk'?

3. 'The Complaints' and 'The Impossible Dead' are books by which Scottish crime writer?

4. Which author, who wrote 'The Gruffalo' and 'The Snail and the Whale', was appointed Children's Laureate in 2011?

5. What is the first book in Stieg Larsson's 'Millennium' trilogy?

6. An almanac called 'Bradshaw's' is associated with which form of transport?

7. Which fictional detective lives in the Swedish town of Ystad?

8. Who won the 2012 Booker Prize for her novel 'Bringing Up the Bodies'?

9. 'What You See Is What You Get' is the title of which businessman's 2010 autobiography?

10. 'Is It Just Me?' was a 2012 bestseller for which actress and comedian?

11. Which Booker Prize-winning author was formerly a team captain on the spoof TV game show 'Shooting Stars'?

12. True or false – American authors are not eligible to win the Booker Prize?

13. 'Billionaire Boy' and 'Ratburger' are children's books written by which comedian?

14. Dorothea Brooke is the central character in which novel by George Eliot?

15. Which food writer and TV chef wrote 'The Kitchen Diaries' and 'Toast: The Story of a Boy's Hunger'?

16. What nationality is the crime writer Jo Nesbo?

17. 'Mud, Sweat, and Tears' is the autobiography of which TV adventurer?

18. What is the first name of Ian Rankin's fictional detective Rebus?

19. Complete the title of the 2013 best-seller by Rachel Joyce: 'The Unlikely Pilgrimage of Harold ...'
    a) Bishop
    c) Fry
    c) Windsor

20. Charles Cumming is a noted author of novels in which genre?
    a) crime
    b) espionage
    c) science fiction

## Answers to Quiz 69: Pot Luck

1. H Gordon Selfridge
2. Birmingham
3. Fight Club
4. Slip
5. Hinduism
6. Shooting
7. Danish
8. Oregon and Maine
9. Genghis Khan
10. Radio 4
11. St Helena
12. French
13. Vince Cable
14. The Apprentice
15. Bonnie Tyler
16. Association of British Travel Agents
17. The Shannon
18. Turin
19. April
20. Gerry Anderson

# Quiz 71: Pot Luck

1. Francis Boulle, Cheska Hull, and Binky Felstead appear in which reality TV show?

2. Who is the patron saint of accountants?

3. What nationality was the inventor of the saxophone, Adolphe Sax?

4. According to the proverb, what is the better part of valour?

5. Which American novelist wrote 'The Naked Lunch'?

6. Which religious leader was born Karol Józef Wojtyła?

7. A saltire gules in a field argent describes the flag of which saint?

8. In British politics, what do the initials DCMS stand for?

9. What are the two London boroughs that start with the letter E?

10. In a game of chess, each player starts with how many pieces?

11. Which Bolton Wanderers footballer retired in 2012 after suffering a heart attack during a game against Tottenham?

12. Which Russian playwright's works include 'The Cherry Orchard', 'Uncle Vanya', and 'The Seagull'?

13. Ernest Hemingway's 'A Farewell To Arms' was set in which conflict?

14. Which director's films include 'Alice in Wonderland', 'Dark Shadows', and 'Frankenweenie'?

15. The Prado museum is in which European capital?

Answers – page 147

16. Is the circumference of the Earth longer at the pole or at the equator?

17. The Kalahari Desert covers portions of which three African countries?

18. The International Monetary Fund is based in which city?

19. Which of these is the name of a comedy series starring Ricky Gervais?
    a) Derek
    b) Malcolm
    c) Norman

20. Which of these football managers has a degree in economics?
    a) Rafa Benitez
    b) Roberto Mancini
    c) Arsene Wenger

## Answers to Quiz 70: Books

1. JK Rowling
2. Sherlock Holmes
3. Ian Rankin
4. Julia Donaldson
5. The Girl with the Dragon Tattoo
6. Railways
7. Kurt Wallander
8. Hilary Mantel
9. Sir Alan Sugar
10. Miranda Hart
11. Will Self
12. True
13. David Walliams
14. Middlemarch
15. Nigel Slater
16. Norwegian
17. Bear Grylls
18. John
19. Fry
20. Espionage

MEDIUM

# Quiz 72: Numbers

1. What is the maximum number of characters allowed in a message on Twitter?

2. What is the name of the 1957 courtroom drama starring Henry Fonda?

3. What is the telephone number for non-urgent enquiries to the police in England and Wales?

4. 'The 400 Blows' was the 1959 debut film from which French new wave director?

5. Which number sits between 7 and 8 on a standard dartboard?

6. '25: The Greatest Hits' is a 2008 compilation album from which Manchester band?

7. 'Fighting Talk' and 'Kermode and Mayo's Film Review' are programmes on which radio station?

8. What was the name of the 2012 film about hitmen and dognappers starring Colin Farrell, Sam Rockwell, and Christopher Walken?

9. In which 2012 film did Jonah Hill and Channing Tatum play cops who posed as school kids to stop the spread of a new drug?

10. What is the fourth event in an Olympic heptathlon?

11. Richard Hannay is the central character in which book by John Buchan, which has also been a long-running West End show?

12. Liz Lemon, Jack Donaghy, and Tracy Morgan were the central characters in which US comedy?

13. In the TV game show 'Bullseye', how much did players have to score in six darts in order to win the star prize?

14. What was the sequel to the film '28 Days Later'?

15. What was the 2009 film remake starring Denzel Washington and John Travolta about a hijacked subway train?

16. How many players can each team have on the court at any one time in a game of basketball?

17. Which artist's painting 'No 5, 1948' was sold in 2006 for $140m?

18. What was the name of the 2010 film directed by Danny Boyle about a climber trapped in a Utah canyon?

19. Who released the 2013 album ' I he 20/20 Experience'?
    a) Justin Bieber  b) Justin Hawkins  c) Justin Timberlake

20. Which number is considered unlucky by Australian cricketers?
    a) 77  b) 87  c) 97

## Answers to Quiz 71: Pot Luck

1.  Made in Chelsea
2.  St Matthew
3.  Belgian
4.  Discretion
5.  William S Burroughs
6.  Pope John Paul II
7.  St Patrick
8.  Department for Culture, Media, and Sport
9.  Ealing and Enfield
10. 16
11. Fabrice Muamba
12. Anton Chekhov
13. World War I
14. Tim Burton
15. Madrid
16. Equator
17. Botswana, South Africa, and Namibia
18. Washington DC
19. Derek
20. Arsene Wenger

# Quiz 73: Pot Luck

1. Complete the proverb: 'nothing is certain but death and ...'

2. Which Aussie comedian hosts the Channel 4 TV show 'The Last Leg'?

3. Who played the title character in the 2013 film 'Hitchcock'?

4. Balsall Heath, Kings Heath, and Moseley are areas of which English city?

5. Eddie Butler and Brian Moore regularly commentate together on which sport?

6. Besides Elizabeth II, who is the only British monarch to celebrate a diamond jubilee?

7. Wilmington is the most populous city in which US state?

8. What is the connection between American playwright Arthur Miller and the World Snooker Championship?

9. Which business tycoon's home on the Caribbean island of Necker was destroyed after a 2011 fire?

10. Which British actor and comedian hosted the Golden Globe Awards in 2010, 2011, and 2012?

11. Which line on the London Underground has the fewest stations?

12. In Shakespeare's 'A Midsummer Night's Dream' who was King of the Fairies?

13. Who was the Queen of the Fairies in the same play?

14. 'Mad, Bad, and Dangerous to Know' is the title of the autobiography of which contemporary explorer and adventurer?

15. Peterhouse is the oldest college at which British university?

16. Manchego is a cheese made from the milk of which animal?

17. In which year was the £1 coin introduced?

18. What was the name of the cruise ship that sank off the coast of Italy in 2012, killing 32 people?

19. In which year did the Cuban Missile Crisis happen?
    a) 1961
    b) 1962
    c) 1963

20. Which coffee shop chain is the sponsor of a major UK literary prize?
    a) Caffe Nero
    b) Costa
    c) Starbucks

**MEDIUM**

## Answers to Quiz 72: Numbers

| | | | |
|---|---|---|---|
| 1. | 140 | 11. | The 39 Steps |
| 2. | Twelve Angry Men | 12. | 30 Rock |
| 3. | 101 | 13. | 101 |
| 4. | François Truffaut | 14. | 28 Weeks Later |
| 5. | 16 | 15. | The Taking of Pelham 123 |
| 6. | Simply Red | 16. | 5 |
| 7. | Radio 5 Live | 17. | Jackson Pollock |
| 8. | Seven Psychopaths | 18. | 127 Hours |
| 9. | 21 Jump Street | 19. | Justin Timberlake |
| 10. | 200m | 20. | 87 |

# Quiz 74: Films

1. Which Irish actor is the star of 'Taken' and 'Taken 2'?

2. Which football team was the subject of the 2009 film 'The Damned United'?

3. Keira Knightley played the title character in which 2012 adaptation of a Russian literary classic?

4. Who directed the 2012 political drama 'Argo'?

5. Daniel Day-Lewis won his first Best Actor Oscar in which film?

6. In the 'Toy Story' films, what sort of object is Hamm?

7. In 'The Best Exotic Marigold Hotel', in which country was the hotel in question located?

8. Which director's films included 'The Big Sleep', 'His Girl Friday', 'Bringing Up Baby', and 'Gentlemen Prefer Blondes'?

9. Jennifer Lawrence played Katniss Everdeen in which 2012 film?

10. Who won the Best Director Oscar in 2013 for 'Life of Pi'?

11. Which Anglo-American actor played the title character in the 2012 film 'The Amazing Spider-Man'?

12. Which brothers shared the Best Director Oscar for 'No Country for Old Men'?

13. Who played the title role in the 2012 drama 'The Master'?

14. Director Peter Jackson is from which country?

15. What sport was the subject of the film 'Any Given Sunday'?

16. Which director's films include 'Punch Drunk Love', 'There Will Be Blood', and 'The Master'?

17. Prior to 'The Artist' in 2012, which was the last black-and-white film to win the Oscar for Best Picture?

18. Christoph Waltz won the Oscar for Best Supporting Actor in 2013 for his role in which film?

19. Which of the following was the title of a 1968 horror film?
    a) 'Barbara's Baby'
    b) 'Rosemary's Baby'
    c) 'Veronica's Baby'

20. The 2012 film 'Silver Linings Playbook' was set in which city?
    a) Cleveland
    b) Philadelphia
    c) Pittsburgh

MEDIUM

## Answers to Quiz 73: Pot Luck

| | | | |
|---|---|---|---|
| 1. | Taxes | 11. | Waterloo and City Line |
| 2. | Adam Hills | 12. | Oberon |
| 3. | Sir Anthony Hopkins | 13. | Titania |
| 4. | Birmingham | 14. | Ranulph Fiennes |
| 5. | Rugby union | 15. | Cambridge |
| 6. | Queen Victoria | 16. | Sheep |
| 7. | Delaware | 17. | 1983 |
| 8. | The Crucible | 18. | Costa Concordia |
| 9. | Richard Branson | 19. | 1962 |
| 10. | Ricky Gervais | 20. | Costa (The Costa Book Awards) |

# Quiz 75: Pot Luck

1. Which inventor is said to have coined the phrase 'Genius is one per cent inspiration, ninety-nine per cent perspiration'?

2. Noted for her impeccable taste in knitwear, Sarah Lund is the main character in which TV crime drama?

3. John and Charles Wesley are associated with the founding of which Christian movement?

4. Which flag is flown when the Queen is in residence at a royal palace?

5. Kansas City is the most populous city in which US state?

6. English footballer and Twitter philosopher Joey Barton joined which French football club in 2012?

7. What is the only London borough that begins with the letter G?

8. What is the county town of Buckinghamshire?

9. In 2009, which body succeeded the House of Lords as the highest judicial authority in Britain?

10. Which Czech-born British playwright's best known works include 'Rosenkrantz and Guildenstern are Dead', 'Arcadia', and 'The Real Thing'?

11. Painted in 1824 and sold at auction in 2012 for £22.4m, 'The Lock' is a work by which English artist?

12. The world-renowned restaurant Noma is in which European city?

13. What was the codename for the German attack on the USSR on 22 June 1941?

14. Who had a longer spell as prime minister, James Callaghan or Gordon Brown?

15. Which US food conglomerate took over British chocolate producer Cadbury in 2011?

16. What is the name of the Norwegian mass-murderer who killed 77 people in 2011?

17. Which movement is based on a book called 'Dianetics: The Modern Science of Mental Health'?

18. Who was Britain's first female poet laureate?

19. Which British musician appeared as one of the Weird Sisters in 'Harry Potter and the Goblet of Fire'?
    a) Damon Albarn
    b) Jarvis Cocker
    c) Noel Gallagher

20. In which field is Daniel Liebeskind a notable name?
    a) architecture
    b) classical music
    c) fashion design

MEDIUM

## Answers to Quiz 74: Films

1. Liam Neeson
2. Leeds United
3. Anna Karenina
4. Ben Affleck
5. My Left Foot
6. A piggy bank
7. India
8. Howard Hawks
9. The Hunger Games
10. Ang Lee
11. Andrew Garfield
12. Joel and Ethan Coen
13. Philip Seymour Hoffman
14. New Zealand
15. American football
16. Paul Thomas Anderson
17. Schindler's List in 1993
18. Django Unchained
19. Rosemary's Baby
20. Philadelphia

# Quiz 76: History part 1

1. Keir Hardie was the first leader of which British political party?

2. In which year did America declare independence from Britain?

3. In 2005, who became the first black Archbishop in the Church of England?

4. Who was the first Plantagenet king of England?

5. In which decade did the Korean War take place?

6. Which conflict between England and France started in 1338?

7. Which US president was associated with a programme called the Great Society?

8. Between 1309 and 1377 the papacy was based in which French city?

9. Who led the Scottish forces to victory at the Battle of Bannockburn?

10. In which country did an uprising called the Boxer Rebellion take place?

11. Which doctrine, named after a US president, promised aid to countries threatened by Communist interference?

12. By what name was the fighting force called the National Front for the Liberation of South Vietnam more commonly known?

13. What was the first country to give women the vote?

14. In 1999, Thabo Mbeki became the president of which country?

Answers – page 157

15. 'Longshanks' was the nickname of which English king?

16. Delano was the middle name of which American president?

17. Who was executed at Fotheringhay Castle in 1587?

18. The first battle of St Albans marked the start of which conflict?

19. King Harald I of Denmark was also known as Harald ...
    a) Blacktooth
    b) Bluetooth
    c) Greytooth

20. In which century did Richard the Lionheart rule England?
    a) 12th century
    b) 13th century
    c) 14th century

MEDIUM

## Answers to Quiz 75: Pot Luck

1.  Thomas Edison
2.  The Killing
3.  Methodism
4.  The Royal Standard
5.  Missouri
6.  Olympique Marseille
7.  Greenwich
8.  Aylesbury
9.  The Supreme Court
10. Tom Stoppard
11. John Constable
12. Copenhagen
13. Barbarossa
14. James Callaghan
15. Kraft
16. Anders Breivik
17. Scientology
18. Carol Ann Duffy
19. Jarvis Cocker
20. Architecture

# Quiz 77: Pot Luck

1.  Who played The Dude in the 1998 cult film 'The Big Lebowski'?

2.  Chorlton-cum-Hardy, Whalley Range, and Withington are areas of which English city?

3.  The headquarters of the United Nations are in which city?

4.  The 2013 film 'Cloud Atlas' is based on a novel by which author?

5.  The much repeated TV sitcom 'Cheers' was set in which city?

6.  Which of the 12 disciples was the brother of John?

7.  True or false – the US state of North Dakota covers a larger area than England?

8.  Bombardier is a company associated with manufacturing what form of transport?

9.  GSK is Britain's largest pharmaceutical company. What do the initials GSK stand for?

10. If the member states of the United Nations were listed alphabetically, which country would be first?

11. ... And which country would be last?

12. Wiener schnitzel is usually made using what type of meat?

13. Which country will host the 2018 FIFA World Cup?

14. In imperial measures, how many ounces make up one stone?

15. What illness is known in America as infectious mononucleosis?

16. 33 copper miners survived for 69 days underground following a mining accident in 2010 in which country?

17. Asad Rauf, Aleem Dar, and Rod Tucker are umpires in which sport?

18. Who was Britain's prime minister at the start of World War II?

19. Graham Coxon, Dave Rowntree, and Alex James are members of which British band?
    a) Blur
    b) Oasis
    c) Pulp

20. What is the lowest rank in the British peerage?
    a) Baron
    b) Earl
    c) Marquis

MEDIUM

## Answers to Quiz 76: History part 1

1. The Labour Party
2. 1776
3. John Sentamu
4. Henry II
5. 1950s
6. The Hundred Years War
7. Lyndon Johnson
8. Avignon
9. Robert the Bruce
10. China
11. Truman Doctrine
12. The Viet Cong
13. New Zealand
14. South Africa
15. Edward I
16. Franklin D Roosevelt
17. Mary, Queen of Scots
18. The Wars of the Roses
19. Harald Bluetooth
20. 12th century

# Quiz 78: Movie Quotations

Identify the films that featured the following memorable lines:

1. 'I feel the need – the need for speed!' (1986)

2. 'I have always depended on the kindness of strangers.' (1951)

3. 'Say "hello" to my little friend!' (1983)

4. 'Keep your friends close, but your enemies closer.' (1974)

5. 'You had me at "hello".' (1996)

6. 'I see dead people.' (1999)

7. 'If you build it, he will come.' (1989)

8. 'Round up the usual suspects.' (1942)

9. 'Hope is a good thing, maybe the best of things, and no good thing ever dies.' (1994)

10. 'A census taker once tried to test me. I ate his liver with some fava beans and a nice Chianti.' (1991)

11. 'Rosebud' (1941)

12. 'Go ahead, make my day.' (1983)

13. 'I'm gonna punch you in the ovary, that's what I'm gonna do. A straight shot, right to the babymaker.' (2004)

14. 'You're gonna need a bigger boat.' (1975)

15. 'I love the smell of napalm in the morning.' (1979)

16. 'Dave, this conversation can serve no purpose anymore. Goodbye.' (1968)

17. 'Hasta la vista, baby.' (1991)

18. 'I find your lack of faith disturbing.' (1977)

19. 'Wax on, right hand. Wax off, left hand. Wax on, wax off.' (1984)

20. 'It takes a great deal of bravery to stand up to your enemies, but a great deal more to stand up to your friends.' (2001)

MEDIUM

## Answers to Quiz 77: Pot Luck

1. Jeff Bridges
2. Manchester
3. New York
4. David Mitchell
5. Boston
6. James (son of Zebedee)
7. True
8. Trains
9. GlaxoSmithKline
10. Afghanistan
11. Zimbabwe
12. Veal
13. Russia
14. 224
15. Glandular fever
16. Chile
17. Cricket
18. Neville Chamberlain
19. Blur
20. Baron

# Quiz 79: Pot Luck

1. Who is the host of TV antique valuation show 'Flog It'?

2. Chequers, the country residence of the UK prime minister, is in which county?

3. Which Coronation Street actor won 'Let's Dance For Comic Relief' in 2013?

4. What type of confectionery is also used to describe an unsatisfactory political compromise?

5. Which British music studios were given Grade II listed status in 2010?

6. England was eliminated from the 2012 UEFA European Championships after losing a penalty shoot-out against which country?

7. Who resigned as leader of the Liberal Democrats in 2006?

8. Nicholas Breakspear is the only English person to hold which post?

9. Rachel Marron and Frank Farmer are the central characters in which 1992 film, which was later turned into a West End musical?

10. Cornelius Lysaght is the BBC's correspondent on which sport?

11. Which British computer scientist created the World Wide Web?

12. In 2012, which sitting Conservative MP controversially appeared on the reality TV show, 'I'm a Celebrity ... Get Me out of Here'?

13. $H_2SO_4$ is the chemical formula for which acid?

14. Queen Elizabeth II is the daughter of which monarch?

15. In 2011, Stephen Harper became prime minister of which country for a third term?

16. Agent J and Agent K are the central characters in which alien-busting film trilogy?

17. What is the middle name of former US president Harry Truman?

18. True or false – the Queen is head of state of Papua New Guinea?

19. Which 1980s pop star was formerly an assistant editor of magazine 'Smash Hits'?
a) Boy George  b) Shakin' Stevens  c) Neil Tennant

20. How many countries take part in the FIFA World Cup finals?
a) 16  b) 24  c) 32

**MEDIUM**

## Answers to Quiz 78: Movie Quotations

1. Top Gun
2. A Streetcar Named Desire
3. Scarface
4. The Godfather: Part II
5. Jerry Maguire
6. The Sixth Sense
7. Field of Dreams
8. Casablanca
9. The Shawshank Redemption
10. The Silence of the Lambs
11. Citizen Kane
12. Sudden Impact
13. Anchorman
14. Jaws
15. Apocalypse Now
16. 2001: A Space Odyssey
17. Terminator II: Judgement Day
18. Star Wars
19. The Karate Kid
20. Harry Potter and the Philosopher's Stone

# Quiz 80: The Queen

1. In which year was the Queen born?

2. What are the Queen's two middle names?

3. In which month does the Queen celebrate her official birthday?

4. Which ceremony marks the official birthday of the sovereign?

5. In which year did the Queen's coronation ceremony take place?

6. What was the name of the Archbishop of Canterbury who conducted the coronation ceremony?

7. Who was the prime minister when the Queen acceded to the throne?

8. Where did the coronation ceremony take place?

9. In 2011, the Queen became the first British monarch since 1911 to visit which country?

10. True or false – the Queen is a patron of the Royal Pigeon Racing Association?

11. Who was the first prime minister to be born during Queen Elizabeth II's reign?

12. True or false – the Queen speaks fluent French?

13. The only time the Queen has had to cancel an overseas tour was in 1974. What was the reason for the cancellation?

14. The Queen has visited which Commonwealth country the most times?

15. How many US presidents have there been during the Queen's reign?

16. Who is the eldest of the Queen's grandchildren?

17. Who is the Queen's youngest grandchild?

18. What was the name of the intruder who broke into the Queen's bedroom in 1982?

19. The Queen received news of her father's death and her accession to the throne while visiting which country?
a) Australia
b) India
c) Kenya

20. What did the Queen do in December 2012 that she had never previously done?
a) attended a cabinet meeting
b) attended an Ashes cricket match
c) attended the Winter Olympics

MEDIUM

## Answers to Quiz 79: Pot Luck

1. Paul Martin
2. Buckinghamshire
3. Anthony Cotton
4. Fudge
5. Abbey Road
6. Italy
7. Charles Kennedy
8. Pope
9. The Bodyguard
10. Horse racing
11. Tim Berners-Lee
12. Nadine Dorries
13. Sulphuric acid
14. King George VI
15. Canada
16. Men in Black
17. S (simply the letter S)
18. True
19. Neil Tennant
20. 32

# Quiz 81: Pot Luck

1. In the Bible, which of the 12 disciples was the brother of Peter?

2. Who was Britain's first female, black Member of Parliament?

3. How were Queen Elizabeth I and Mary, Queen of Scots related?

4. What are the six official languages of the United Nations?

5. Broadcaster Clare Balding is the daughter of a successful trainer in which sport?

6. Who is the actress wife of 007 actor Daniel Craig?

7. Trenton is the most populous city in which American state?

8. Which bespectacled broadcaster is the BBC's political editor?

9. Which long-running US drama was set in the fictional County General Hospital in Chicago?

10. What is the name of the character played by John Hamm in the TV drama 'Mad Men'?

11. Which female singer had five US number one hits from her album 'Teenage Dream'?

12. The 2012 film animation 'Brave' is set in which country?

13. Stan, Francine, Roger, Steve, and Hayley Smith are characters in which American animated comedy?

14. 'Habemus Papam Franciscum' was the first Tweet from which spiritual leader?

15. Animated characters Wallace and Gromit are especially fond of what type of cheese?

16. Which country is home to the world's largest railway network?

17. On which TV series will you see villainous creatures called Weeping Angels?

18. Which Hollywood actress is married to country singer Keith Urban?

19. Quinine is used chiefly in the treatment of which disease?
    a) malaria
    b) tuberculosis
    c) whooping cough

20. What was the first sequel to the 2008 film 'Twilight'?
    a) New Moon
    b) Eclipse
    c) Breaking Dawn

## Answers to Quiz 80: The Queen

1. 1926
2. Alexandra Mary
3. June
4. Trooping the Colour
5. 1953
6. Dr Geoffrey Fisher
7. Winston Churchill
8. Westminster Abbey
9. The Republic of Ireland
10. True
11. Tony Blair
12. True
13. A general election had been called
14. Canada
15. 12
16. Peter Phillips
17. James, Viscount Severn (born 2007)
18. Michael Fagan
19. Kenya
20. She attended a cabinet meeting

MEDIUM

# Quiz 82: Pop Music part 1

1. Danny O'Donoghue is the frontman of which Irish rock band?

2. Perrie Edwards, Jesy Nelson, Leigh-Anne Pinnock, and Jade Thirlwall are members of which band?

3. Who topped the charts in 2012 with 'Payphone'?

4. Which female singer appeared in concerts around the world between 2007 and 2009 on the 'Good Girl Gone Bad' tour?

5. 'Life' was the 2010 autobiography by which member of the Rolling Stones?

6. 'The Queen Is Dead', 'Meat Is Murder', and 'Hatful of Hollow' are albums by which seminal Manchester band?

7. Which TV talent-show star topped the charts in 2009 with a cover of Snow Patrol's song 'Run'?

8. The 1988 hit 'Desire' was which group's first UK number one single?

9. According to the Sunday Times Rich List, who was the wealthiest living musician in 2013?

10. What is the biggest selling UK single of all time?

11. The chart-topping 'Born to Die' was the 2012 debut album from which American singer-songwriter?

12. David Lee Roth is the lead vocalist with which veteran US rock band?

13. Who is the lead vocalist with the Irish band The Divine Comedy?

14. Which English singer was named as one of 'Time' magazine's 100 most influential people of 2012?

Answers – page 169

15. Pop band the Kings of Convenience and singer Lene Marlin are from which European country?

16. What is the first name of former frontman of The Smiths, Morrissey?

17. Which pop star's 1993 world tour was called 'The Girlie Show'?

18. In which decade was the first ever UK singles chart launched?

19. What was the title of a 2010 album by Arcade Fire?
    a) The City
    b) The Country
    c) The Suburbs

20. Complete the title of a 2011 hit by Maroon 5: 'Moves Like ...'
    a) Bowie
    b) Jackson
    c) Jagger

**MEDIUM**

## Answers to Quiz 81: Pot Luck

1. Andrew
2. Diane Abbott
3. They were cousins
4. English, French, Arabic, Chinese, Russian, Spanish
5. Horse racing
6. Rachel Weisz
7. New Jersey
8. Nick Robinson
9. ER
10. Don Draper
11. Katy Perry
12. Scotland
13. American Dad!
14. Pope Francis
15. Wensleydale
16. USA
17. Dr Who
18. Nicole Kidman
19. Malaria
20. New Moon

# Quiz 83: Pot Luck

1. Which French monarch was known as the 'Sun King'?

2. What body is responsible for operating, maintaining, and improving England's motorway network?

3. Rick Deckard is the central character in which 1982 sci-fi classic?

4. What sport would you expect to see at grounds called Eden Gardens, the Gabba, and Sabina Park?

5. Excluding Alaska, what is the largest state of the USA by area?

6. In football, 'elfmeter' is the German word for what?

7. What is the name of the app that enables a user to identify a song by holding up their phone to a speaker playing that song?

8. Which husband and wife discovered the chemical elements radium and polonium?

9. What is the only one of the four great offices of state in British politics that has never been occupied by a woman?

10. Bechuanaland is the former name of which African country?

11. In 2012, actress Carey Mulligan married the lead singer of which best-selling band?

12. Writer Franz Kafka was born in which European capital?

13. Hong Kong is one of China's two Special Administrative Regions. Which former Portuguese colony is the other?

14. Who played Batman in the 1997 film 'Batman and Robin'?

15. The tombstone of which politician read, 'I am ready to meet my Maker. Whether my Maker is prepared for the great ordeal of meeting me is another matter'?

16. Which author, who was played by Nicole Kidman in a 2002 film, drowned herself in the River Ouse on 28 March 1941?

17. Which former newspaper editor hosts the TV show 'The Daily Politics'?

18. Which island group lies 28 miles south-west of Land's End in Cornwall?

19. The Caribbean islands of Bonaire, Sint Eustatius, and Saba are overseas territories of which country?
    a) France
    b) The Netherlands
    c) Portugal

20. Which manager of the England football team was cruelly dubbed 'The wally with the brolly'?
    a) Steve McClaren
    b) Bobby Robson
    c) Graham Taylor

## Answers to Quiz 82: Pop Music part 1

| | |
|---|---|
| 1. The Script | 11. Lana del Rey |
| 2. Little Mix | 12. Van Halen |
| 3. Maroon 5 | 13. Neil Hannon |
| 4. Rihanna | 14. Adele |
| 5. Keith Richards | 15. Norway |
| 6. The Smiths | 16. Steven |
| 7. Leona Lewis | 17. Madonna |
| 8. U2 | 18. 1950s |
| 9. Paul McCartney | 19. The Suburbs |
| 10. 'Candle in the Wind 1997' by Elton John | 20. Jagger |

MEDIUM

# Quiz 84: Colours

1. What is the name of the 2012 album by US R&B star Frank Ocean?

2. What 1986 film directed by David Lynch was also the title of a 2012 song by Lana Del Rey?

3. Which singer, who died in 2006, was laid in state in a 24-carat gold coffin?

4. What is the nickname of the Belgium national football team?

5. The Blue House is the residence of the president of which Asian country?

6. What is the name of Woody Allen's 1985 Depression-era drama?

7. Which England goalkeeper's howler gifted the USA a point in a 2010 World Cup match?

8. Which charity event was held for the first time on 5 February 1988?

9. Which actress played James Bond's love interest, Vesper Lynd, in the 2006 film 'Casino Royale'?

10. Natalie Portman won an Oscar in 2011 for her performance in which film?

11. What colour kit is worn by the Pakistan team in one-day cricket matches?

12. 'Tired of Being Alone', 'Let's Stay Together', and 'I'm Still In Love with You' were hits for which soul singer?

13. In American politics, what colour is associated with the Republican Party?

14. What is the name of the Terrence Malick film focusing on the battle of Guadalcanal in World War II?

15. 2003's 'Where Is The Love' was the first UK number one hit single for which group?

16. Which NFL team won the first Super Bowl?

17. Alex DeLarge is the central character in which book which was made into a controversial film in 1971?

18. What is the name of the flag flown by British merchant navy ships?

19. 'Vanessa atalanta' is the Latin name for which common butterfly?

20. Which British actor played Colin Clark in 'My Week With Marilyn' and Marius Pontmercy in 'Les Miserables'?

## Answers to Quiz 83: Pot Luck

1. Louis XIV
2. Highways Agency
3. Blade Runner
4. Cricket
5. Texas
6. A penalty
7. Shazam
8. Pierre and Marie Curie
9. Chancellor of the Exchequer
10. Botswana
11. Mumford and Sons (Marcus Mumford)
12. Prague
13. Macau
14. George Clooney
15. Winston Churchill
16. Virginia Woolf
17. Andrew Neil
18. Isles of Scilly
19. The Netherlands
20. Steve McClaren

MEDIUM

# Quiz 85: Pot Luck

1. In the Bible, who was the only one of the original 12 disciples whose name started with the letter B?

2. Who is the only British monarch to have celebrated a diamond wedding anniversary?

3. Which South American country is also the title of a 1985 science-fiction fantasy film directed by Terry Gilliam?

4. 'The Rite of Spring' is by which Russian-born composer?

5. Which British broadcaster and journalist succeeded Larry King as the host of CNN's 'Tonight' programme?

6. What is the official language of the Olympic Games?

7. Who was the only US President to be sworn in on an aeroplane?

8. Who played Nelson Mandela in the 2009 film 'Invictus'?

9. 'Wolfie' is the nickname of which darts champion?

10. In 2010, a bidder on eBay paid $2.63 million for lunch with which American investor and business guru?

11. Who was the last permanent leader of the Liberal Democrats before Nick Clegg?

12. Whom did Roy Hodgson succeed as permanent manager of the England football team?

13. The term 'paparazzi' was introduced into the English language via which 1960 film directed by Federico Fellini?

14. Which ancient Greek playwright wrote 'Oedipus the King' and 'Antigone'?

15. What is the third largest city in Spain by population?

16. What is the building at 1 Canada Square also known as?

17. Scottish banknotes are issued by which three banks?

18. 'Oh, wow. Oh, wow. Oh, wow' were the last words of which technological innovator who died in 2011?

19. The River Danube flows into which sea?
    a) Black Sea
    b) Baltic Sea
    c) North Sea

20. In poker, which of the following hands ranks highest?
    a) full house
    b) quad aces
    c) nut flush

**MEDIUM**

## Answers to Quiz 84: Colours

| | | | |
|---|---|---|---|
| 1. | Channel Orange | 11. | Green |
| 2. | Blue Velvet | 12. | Al Green |
| 3. | James Brown | 13. | Red |
| 4. | The Red Devils | 14. | The Thin Red Line |
| 5. | South Korea | 15. | The Black Eyed Peas |
| 6. | The Purple Rose of Cairo | 16. | Green Bay Packers |
| 7. | Robert Green | 17. | A Clockwork Orange |
| 8. | Red Nose Day | 18. | Red Ensign |
| 9. | Eva Green | 19. | Red Admiral |
| 10. | Black Swan | 20. | Eddie Redmayne |

# Quiz 86: Famous Richards

Identify the following famous Richards from the clues below:

1. Jockey who won the Grand National on West Tip and Miinnehoma.

2. Bald-headed host of TV's 'The Crystal Maze'.

3. The real name of Beatle Ringo Starr.

4. American actor, born in 1949, whose middle name is Tiffany.

5. Composer whose work is commemorated at the Bayreuth Festival.

6. Star of 'Ever Decreasing Circles' who died in February 2013.

7. One of the main characters in the TV sitcom 'Happy Days'.

8. Veteran Indian-born singer who had more UK top ten albums in the 1980s than any other artist.

9. The first cricketer to take 400 Test wickets.

10. Vice-president of the USA from 2001 until 2009.

11. Monarch whose remains were discovered under a Leicester car park.

12. Legendary Antiguan cricketer named one of Wisden's Five Cricketers of the Century.

13. The lead singer with indie rockers The Verve.

14. Actor who played Maurice Moss in the TV comedy 'The IT Crowd' and directed the film 'Submarine'.

Answers – page 177

15. Architect who designed the Pompidou Centre in Paris and the Lloyd's Building in London.

16. A member of the Brit Award winning pop band Steps.

17. The first person to speak on Channel 4.

18. Actor who appeared in 'American Grafitti', 'Jaws', and 'Close Encounters of the Third Kind'.

19. In 1995 he became the second Welshman to win the World Darts Championship.

20. American theoretical physicist, known for his work in quantum mechanics, who won the Nobel Prize in 1965.

**MEDIUM**

## Answers to Quiz 85: Pot Luck

1. Bartholomew
2. Queen Elizabeth II
3. Brazil
4. Igor Stravinsky
5. Piers Morgan
6. French
7. Lyndon Johnson
8. Morgan Freeman
9. Martin Adams
10. Warren Buffett
11. Menzies Campbell
12. Fabio Capello
13. La Dolce Vita
14. Sophocles
15. Valencia
16. Canary Wharf
17. Bank of Scotland, Royal Bank of Scotland, and Clydesdale Bank
18. Steve Jobs
19. Black Sea
20. Quad aces

# Quiz 87: Pot Luck

1. In which sport are the Baltimore Ravens and Denver Broncos notable teams?

2. Which 19th-century English engineer reportedly smoked 40 cigars a day?

3. Between 1993 and 2003, Jean Chrétien was the prime minister of which country?

4. What is the Japanese movie monster 'Gojira' known as to English-speaking audiences?

5. In the human body, by what name is the bone called the clavicle more commonly known?

6. Which British group, whose name is also that of a town in France, recorded the albums 'Fox Base Alpha', 'Words and Music', and 'Tales from Turnpike House'?

7. What vegetable is used in a dish cooked 'Florentine' style?

8. Who played Hermione Granger in the 'Harry Potter' films?

9. Which actor played the foul-mouthed spin doctor Malcolm Tucker in parliamentary comedy 'The Thick of It'?

10. 'Anthem for Doomed Youth' was a sonnet written by which First World War poet?

11. Which sport was the subject of the film 'Seabiscuit'?

12. Which British actor celebrated his 80th birthday on 14 March 2013?

13. How wide in yards are the goalposts on a full-size football pitch?

14. Bacchus was the Roman god of revelry, theatre and wine. Who was his Greek equivalent?

Answers – page 179

15. A man with the letters KG after his name is a member of which order of chivalry?

16. Which famous Spanish building takes its name from the Arabic for 'the red one'?

17. Caboc cheese originates from which country?

18. Phobos and Deimos are moons of which planet of the Solar System?

19. Which 'Charlie's Angels' actress has enjoyed success in the wine world after launching an award-winning Pinot Grigio?

20. Which economist's best known work is 'The General Theory of Employment, Interest, and Money'?
    a) Milton Friedman
    b) John Maynard Keynes
    c) Adam Smith

MEDIUM

## Answers to Quiz 86: Famous Richards

1.  Richard Dunwoody
2.  Richard O'Brien
3.  Richard Starkey
4.  Richard Gere
5.  Richard Wagner
6.  Richard Briers
7.  Richie Cunningham
8.  Cliff Richard
9.  Sir Richard Hadlee
10. Richard 'Dick' Cheney
11. Richard III
12. Sir Viv Richards
13. Richard Ashcroft
14. Richard Ayoade
15. Richard Rogers
16. Clare Richards
17. Richard Whiteley
18. Richard Dreyfuss
19. Richie Burnett
20. Richard Feynman

# Quiz 88: Science and Technology

1. Who wrote the best-selling but little-read book 'A Brief History of Time'?

2. Often used to make darts, which element of the periodic table has the atomic number 74 and the symbol W?

3. Which English scientists discovered the structure of DNA?

4. Otology is the branch of medical science that deals with which part of the body?

5. What is the nearest star to the Earth?

6. Which chemical element has the symbol P, atomic number 15, and takes its name from the Greek for 'light-bearing'?

7. What was the name of the mission that saw Yuri Gagarin become the first man in space?

8. The Large Hadron Collider particle accelerator lies underneath the border of which two countries?

9. Which English astronomer founded the Jodrell Bank Observatory?

10. True or false – Japanese technology company Nintendo was founded in the 19th century?

11. What name is given to regions of space where gravity is so powerful that even light cannot escape?

12. What is the boiling point of water in Fahrenheit?

13. What does the acronym 'laser' stand for?

14. Costing around £85 billion, what is the most expensive object ever made?

15. Which four-letter word is used to describe a website that allows anyone to add or amend its content?

16. Whose law states that the number of transistors per silicon chip doubles every two years?

17. Which American astronomer, who was the first to prove that there are galaxies outside the Milky Way, gave his name to a famous space telescope?

18. Which science-fiction writer devised the Three Laws of Robotics?

19. Gordon Moore and Robert Noyce founded which giant technology company?
a) Apple  b) Intel  c) Panasonic

20. Endocrinology is a branch of medicine that deals with what?
a) the skin  b) hormones  c) nerves

MEDIUM

## Answers to Quiz 87: Pot Luck

1.  American football
2.  Isambard Kingdom Brunel
3.  Canada
4.  Godzilla
5.  Collar bone
6.  Saint Etienne
7.  Spinach
8.  Emma Watson
9.  Peter Capaldi
10. Wilfred Owen
11. Horse racing
12. Sir Michael Caine
13. Eight yards
14. Dionysus
15. The Order of the Garter
16. Alhambra
17. Scotland
18. Mars
19. Drew Barrymore
20. John Maynard Keynes

# Quiz 89: Pot Luck

1. The giant CN Tower is in which North American city?

2. The NBA is the governing body of which American sport?

3. What is the English meaning of the Latin phrase 'Corpus Christi'?

4. Which racehorse owner's colours are a purple body with gold braiding, scarlet sleeves, and a black velvet cap with gold fringe?

5. Which saint was the first Archbishop of Canterbury?

6. Robert Menzies is the longest serving prime minister of which country?

7. Which Lib Dem MP was jailed in 2013 after lying about driving points?

8. What is the name of the MP's ex-wife who was also jailed?

9. Roddy Doyle's books known as 'The Barrytown Trilogy' are set in which city?

10. Hainaut and Limberg are provinces of which European country?

11. East Pakistan is the former name of which country?

12. How many metatarsal bones are found in a human foot?

13. What is the hardest substance found in the human body?

14. Which country has the largest road network in the world?

15. The Indian Pacific is a massive railway line in which country?

16. Are the goalposts wider on a football pitch or a rugby pitch?

17. Ashton Gate is the home ground of which English football club?

18. 'Running My Life' was the title of a 2012 autobiography by which athlete, politician, and administrator?

19. In terms of area, what is the largest of New York's five boroughs?
    a) Brooklyn
    b) The Bronx
    c) Queens

20. On a Monopoly board, what colour are the Euston Road, Angel Islington, and Pentonville Road?
    a) light blue
    b) purple
    c) orange

MEDIUM

## Answers to Quiz 88: Science and Technology

1. Stephen Hawking
2. Tungsten
3. Francis Crick and James Watson
4. The ear
5. Proxima Centauri
6. Phosphorus
7. Vostok 1
8. France and Switzerland
9. Sir Bernard Lovell
10. True (in 1889)
11. Black holes

12. 212°F
13. Light Amplification by the Stimulated Emission of Radiation
14. The International Space Station
15. Wiki
16. Moore's Law
17. Edwin Hubble
18. Isaac Asimov
19. Intel
20. Hormones

# Quiz 90: Scotland

1. Robert Gordon University is in which city?

2. Which Scottish town was granted city status in 2012? ·

3. In Glasgow, what are The Barrowlands, Kings Tut's Wah Wah Hut, and Nice N Sleazy?

4. Muckle Roe, Unst, and West Burra are part of which Scottish island group?

5. In a court case, what are the three verdicts that can be delivered by a Scottish jury?

6. What title is given to the person who chairs the proceedings in the Scottish Parliament?

7. Scottish sailor Alexander Selkirk was the inspiration for which literary character?

8. True or false – the first two prime ministers of Canada were born in Scotland?

9. Which Scottish football team plays its home games at Tannadice Park?

10. Which London-born Scottish actress won a Best Supporting Actress Oscar for her performance in 2007 drama Michael Clayton?

11. Prior to Gordon Brown, who was the last Scottish-born British prime minister?

12. Balmoral Castle is in which Scottish council area?

13. Who was Scotland's First Minister from 2001 to 2007?

14. Which Paisley-born law graduate starred alongside Jennifer Aniston in the 2010 film 'The Bounty Hunter'?

15. The Burrell Collection and the Hunterian are museums in which Scottish city?

16. In which year did the first elections to the Scottish Parliament take place?

17. Who are the two Scots to have won the Formula One World Drivers' Championship?

18. Skibo Castle was the home of which Scottish-born industrialist and philanthropist?

19. In which decade was the Scottish anthem 'Flower of Scotland' written?
    a) 1760s
    b) 1860s
    c) 1960s

20. How many members sit in the Scottish Parliament?
    a) 89
    b) 109
    c) 129

MEDIUM

## Answers to Quiz 89: Pot Luck

1. Toronto
2. Basketball
3. Body of Christ
4. The Queen
5. St Augustine
6. Australia
7. Chris Huhne
8. Vicky Pryce
9. Dublin
10. Belgium
11. Bangladesh
12. Five
13. Enamel (in teeth)
14. USA
15. Australia
16. Football
17. Bristol City
18. Sebastian Coe
19. Queens
20. Light blue

# Quiz 91: Pot Luck

1. Which member of rock group Queen and part-time astronomer was offered a position at the Jodrell Bank Observatory?

2. What is the fifth book in the 'Harry Potter' series?

3. Who comes next on this list: Roy Plomley, Michael Parkinson, Sue Lawley?

4. Which London tube line runs from Walthamstow to Brixton?

5. Which bone connects the forearm bones to the shoulder joint?

6. Whose third law states, 'Whenever a force acts, an equal force acts in the opposite direction'?

7. Is sea water slightly acidic or slightly alkaline?

8. In a computer, what do the initials CPU stand for?

9. Who played the title character in the 1998 film 'There's Something About Mary'?

10. Which European country shares borders with Germany, Poland, Slovakia, and Austria?

11. Which African country shares land borders with Tunisia, Libya, Morocco, Mali, Niger, Mauritania, and Western Sahara?

12. Which country has received 'nul points' the most times in the history of the Eurovision Song Contest?

13. Which composer wrote the scores to the 'Star Wars' and 'Indiana Jones' films?

14. Which children's organization was founded in Glasgow by Sir William Alexander Smith in 1883?

Answers – page 187

15. 'Now is the winter of our discontent' are the opening words of which Shakespeare play?

16. Lt CD Lucas was the first recipient of which military honour?

17. 'The Whitsun Weddings' is a collection by which British poet?

18. Danzig is the German name for which Polish city?

19. How many tiles are in a standard domino set?
    a) 18
    b) 28
    c) 38

20. In which decade were the classic films 'Citizen Kane' and 'The Maltese Falcon' released?
    a) 1930s
    b) 1940s
    c) 1950s

MEDIUM

## Answers to Quiz 90: Scotland

1. Aberdeen
2. Perth
3. Nightclubs and music venues
4. Shetland
5. Guilty, not guilty, and not proven
6. The Presiding Officer
7. Robinson Crusoe
8. True
9. Dundee United
10. Tilda Swinton
11. Tony Blair
12. Aberdeenshire
13. Jack McConnell
14. Gerard Butler
15. Glasgow
16. 1999
17. Jackie Stewart and Jim Clark
18. Andrew Carnegie
19. 1960s
20. 129

# Quiz 92: Victoria and Albert

Identify the famous Victorias and Alberts from the clues below:

1. Singer-turned-fashion designer and one of the 100 most influential women in the UK in 2012 according to the radio programme 'Woman's Hour'.

2. Algerian-born author who wrote 'The Plague' and 'The Outsider'.

3. Cyclist who won the gold medal in the keirin event at the 2012 Olympics.

4. The title of a 2008 romantic comedy directed by Woody Allen starring Javier Bardem and Scarlett Johansson.

5. Salford-born Oscar-nominated actor who appeared alongside Julia Roberts in 'Erin Brockovich'.

6. Racing driver-turned-journalist who hosts TV motoring show 'Fifth Gear'.

7. American actress best known for playing Pam Ewing in 'Dallas'.

8. Schoolgirl played by Matt Lucas in the TV comedy 'Little Britain'.

9. The first black footballer to play in the FA Cup final.

10. Writer, poker player, and host of TV quiz show 'Only Connect'.

11. American who produced many of the James Bond films.

12. Singer whose only UK top 20 hit was 'Free Electric Band'.

13. Actress who played Eric Morecambe's mother in the 2011 TV drama 'Eric and Ernie'.

14. Politician who was the room-mate of Tommy Lee Jones while studying at Harvard.

15. Veteran British soap-opera character played by Jack Howarth.

16. Belarussian tennis player who won the Australian Open in 2012 and 2013.

17. American actor, whose real surname is Einstein, who voiced Marlin in 'Finding Nemo' and starred in 2011 crime drama 'Drive'.

18. South African cricketer whose younger brother, Morne, also plays international cricket for the Proteas.

19. Swedish model, actress, singer, and television personality, born in 1974.

20. Actress best known for playing Yvette Carte-Blanche in BBC comedy "Allo, 'Allo'.

**MEDIUM**

## Answers to Quiz 91: Pot Luck

1. Brian May
2. Harry Potter and the Order of the Phoenix
3. Kirsty Young (hosts of 'Desert Island Discs')
4. Victoria line
5. Humerus
6. Isaac Newton's
7. Slightly alkaline
8. Central processing unit
9. Cameron Diaz
10. Czech Republic
11. Algeria
12. Norway
13. John Williams
14. The Boys' Brigade
15. Richard III
16. The Victoria Cross
17. Philip Larkin
18. Gdansk
19. 28
20. 1940s

# Quiz 93: Pot Luck

1. In Texas hold 'em poker, how many cards does each player start with?

2. Who directed the classic 1925 silent film 'Battleship Potemkin'?

3. True or false – artist Tracey Emin has never won the Turner Prize?

4. In computing, how many bytes are in a gigabyte?

5. What is the first name of TV detective 'Lewis'?

6. Who wrote the children's book 'The Tales of Beedle the Bard'?

7. Which footballer won his 100th cap in England's 2013 match against Brazil?

8. If the capital cities of member countries of the European Union were listed alphabetically, which city would come last?

9. Madras is the former name of which Indian city?

10. 'Modern Life Is Rubbish', 'The Great Escape', and 'Think Tank' are albums by which British band?

11. Which monarch was known as 'The wisest fool in Christendom'?

12. 'Carrie' was the debut novel from which horror writer?

13. Which US state capital takes its name from the French for 'red stick'?

14. 'Tender is the Night' was the final completed novel by which American author?

Answers – page 191

15. Which member of the European Union has a map of the country on its national flag?

16. Leopoldville is the former name of which African city?

17. Which tennis tournament is played at Roland Garros?

18. True or false – more than half the bones in the human body are in the hands and feet?

19. Complete the title of the 1902 novel by Edith Nesbit: 'Five Children and ...'
    a) Him
    b) It
    c) Them

20. In yards, how long is a cricket pitch?
    a) 20 yards
    b) 21 yards
    c) 22 yards

MEDIUM

## Answers to Quiz 92: Victoria and Albert

1. Victoria Beckham
2. Albert Camus
3. Victoria Pendleton
4. Vicky Cristina Barcelona
5. Albert Finney
6. Vicky Butler Henderson
7. Victoria Principal
8. Vicky Pollard
9. Albert Johansson
10. Victoria Coren
11. Albert 'Cubby' Broccoli
12. Albert Hammond
13. Victoria Wood
14. Al Gore
15. Albert Tatlock
16. Victoria Azarenka
17. Albert Brooks
18. Albie Morkel
19. Victoria Silvstedt
20. Vicki Michelle

# Quiz 94: Sport

1. Which was the last country to win football's World Cup on home soil?

2. Which stadium hosted the 2013 Champions League final?

3. Which team won rugby league's Super League Grand Final in both 2011 and 2012?

4. Whom did Andy Murray beat in the 2012 Olympic tennis final?

5. Who is the only Canadian to have won the World Snooker Championship?

6. Dai Greene won gold in the 2011 World Athletics Championships in which event?

7. Which 59-year-old golfer lost a play-off to Stewart Cink at the 2009 Open Championship?

8. Which team from the fourth tier of English football reached the final of the 2013 League Cup?

9. Which horse retired in 2012 following an unbeaten 14-race career that included wins in the 2011 2,000 Guineas and the 2012 Champion Stakes?

10. In 2013, Mauricio Pochettino replaced Nigel Adkins as manager of which English football club?

11. Jenson Button won the Formula One World Drivers' Championship in 2009 driving for which team?

12. How many matches must a player win to be crowned men's singles champion at Wimbledon?

13. Which Scot won the World Snooker Championship in 2006?

14. In darts, what is the lowest score that cannot be finished in three darts?

15. Who are the two Swedish players to have won the men's singles at Wimbledon?

16. Franklin's Gardens is the home ground of which English rugby union team?

17. Who was the captain of the England cricket team that won the 2005 Ashes series against Australia?

18. In feet, how long is a full-size snooker table?

19. How many teams took part in the 2013 season of rugby league's Super League?
a) 10  b) 12  c) 14

20. Which event at the 2012 Olympics was hosted at Lord's cricket ground?
a) archery  b) beach volleyball  c) shooting

MEDIUM

## Answers to Quiz 93: Pot Luck

1. Two
2. Sergei Eisenstein
3. True
4. 1,000,000,000
5. Robbie
6. JK Rowling
7. Ashley Cole
8. Zagreb
9. Chennai
10. Blur
11. James I (James VI of Scotland)
12. Stephen King
13. Baton Rouge
14. F Scott Fitzgerald
15. Cyprus
16. Kinshasa
17. French Open
18. True
19. It
20. 22 yards

# Quiz 95: Pot Luck

1. In law and order, what do the initials IPCC stand for?

2. The classic film 'Citizen Kane' was based on which newspaper mogul and businessman?

3. All-rounder Vernon Philander plays international cricket for which country?

4. Maria Sklodowska was the birth name of which Nobel-winning scientist?

5. Laura Robson, Heather Watson, and Anne Keothavong are notable British performers in which sport?

6. 'Neither a borrower nor a lender be' is a line from which Shakespeare play?

7. Ben Affleck and Matt Damon won a Best Screenplay Oscar in 1998 for which film?

8. Richard Kiel played which giant James Bond baddie?

9. 'The Ring Cycle' is a series of four operas by which composer?

10. Which English poet, who died in the First World War, wrote 'Grantchester' and 'The Soldier'?

11. If the capital cities of member countries of the European Union were listed alphabetically, which city would come first?

12. Which politician is known in Argentina as 'La Dama de Hierro'?

13. Which country in the world is covered by the largest area of forests?

14. Which US president uttered the phrase, 'Read my lips, no new taxes'?

15. Which UK political party has the initials TUV?

16. Which Spice Girl has been a judge on the TV talent show 'America's Got Talent'?

17. Which Brontë sister wrote the novels 'Shirley' and 'Villette'?

18. What was the former name of Ho Chi Minh City?

19. Albert II became the king of which country in 1993?
    a) Belgium
    b) Netherlands
    c) Sweden

20. The European Union is comprised of how many countries?
    a) 26
    b) 27
    c) 28

**MEDIUM**

## Answers to Quiz 94: Sport

1. France
2. Wembley
3. Leeds Rhinos
4. Roger Federer
5. Cliff Thorburn
6. 400m hurdles
7. Tom Watson
8. Bradford City
9. Frankel
10. Southampton
11. Brawn
12. Seven
13. Graeme Dott
14. 159
15. Bjorn Borg and Stefan Edberg
16. Northampton Saints
17. Michael Vaughan
18. 12 feet
19. 14
20. Archery

# Quiz 96: South America

1. What are the 12 sovereign states of mainland South America?

2. Which was the first South American country to win football's World Cup?

3. What nationality is the Nobel-prize-winning novelist Gabriel García Márquez?

4. Which territory of South America is part of the European Union?

5. In 1973, the government of President Salvador Allende was overthrown in a military coup in which country?

6. Dutch is the official language of which South American country?

7. Luiz Inácio Lula da Silva was the long-time president of which country?

8. What is the largest city in South America?

9. What are the two countries of South America that do not share a border with Brazil?

10. Cape Horn, the most southerly point of South America, lies in which country?

11. English is the official language of which South American country?

12. What is the smallest independent country in South America?

13. What are the four South American countries to have hosted football's World Cup?

14. The flags of Colombia, Ecuador, and Venezuela all feature stripes of which three colours?

15. The eighth largest country in the world by area lies in South America. Which country is it?

16. Who are the four South Americans to have won the Formula One Drivers' Championship?

17. What is the capital city of Paraguay?

18. The world's highest waterfall, Angel Falls, is in which South American country?

19. The port city of Fray Bentos is in which country?
    a) Argentina
    b) Colombia
    c) Uruguay

20. Excluding Brazil, which country in South America has the largest population?
    a) Argentina
    b) Chile
    c) Colombia

MEDIUM

## Answers to Quiz 95: Pot Luck

1. Independent Police Complaints Commission
2. William Randolph Hearst
3. South Africa
4. Marie Curie
5. Tennis
6. Hamlet
7. Good Will Hunting
8. Jaws
9. Richard Wagner
10. Rupert Brooke
11. Amsterdam
12. Margaret Thatcher
13. Russia
14. George H W Bush
15. Traditional Unionist Voice
16. Mel B
17. Charlotte Brontë
18. Saigon
19. Belgium
20. 28

# Quiz 97: Pot Luck

1. Which American abstract painter was dubbed 'Jack the Dripper' by 'Time' magazine?

2. Which Chinese philosopher is also known as K'ung-fu-tzu?

3. Which Polish-born author, who died in 1924, wrote the novels 'Lord Jim' and 'Nostromo'?

4. Who captained Europe's 2012 Ryder Cup-winning team?

5. What are the three European Union capitals that start with the letter V?

6. The 'Head to Head' and the 'Supermatch Game' were rounds in which popular TV quiz show?

7. Which veteran British rockers celebrated their 50th anniversary in 2012?

8. Which French-sounding city is the capital of the US state of Vermont?

9. What does the letter D in the economic organization OECD stand for?

10. Which element of the periodic table has the atomic number 19 and the chemical symbol K?

11. Which country won the Cricket World Cup for the first time in 1983?

12. 'Tomorrow Is a Latter Day' and 'Joseph Smith American Moses' are songs from which hit West End musical?

13. An internet domain ending with the letters .de is from which country?

14. Which name connects a Bond girl from the film 'Thunderball' and a 2012 hit for Jessie J?

15. 'Domenica' is the Italian word for which day of the week?

16. Vine Street and Bow Street are two of the three orange properties on a Monopoly board. What is the third?

17. Which three colours make up the flag of Algeria?

18. Of what is apiology the study?

19. Which country won the Rugby World Cup for the first time in 1995?
    a) Australia
    b) France
    c) South Africa

20. Who was the host of the TV talent show 'The Great British Sewing Bee'?
    a) Sue Perkins
    b) Claudia Winkleman
    c) Holly Willoughby

MEDIUM

## Answers to Quiz 96: South America

1. Argentina, Bolivia, Brazil, Chile, Colombia, Ecuador, Guyana, Paraguay, Peru, Suriname, Uruguay, and Venezuela
2. Uruguay
3. Colombian
4. French Guiana
5. Chile
6. Suriname
7. Brazil
8. Sao Paulo in Brazil
9. Chile and Ecuador
10. Chile
11. Guyana
12. Suriname
13. Argentina, Brazil, Chile, and Uruguay
14. Yellow, blue, and red
15. Argentina
16. Juan Manuel Fangio, Emerson Fittipaldi, Nelson Piquet, and Ayrton Senna
17. Asuncion
18. Venezuela
19. Uruguay
20. Colombia

# Quiz 98: Wales

1. Laver bread is a Welsh delicacy made from what?

2. Whom did Carwyn Jones succeed as First Minister of Wales in 2009?

3. What is the name of the bridge that links Anglesey and the Welsh mainland?

4. Which James Bond actor was born in Colwyn Bay?

5. The Welsh Grand National horse race is run at which course?

6. Which town in Mid Wales plays host to an international Jazz festival?

7. Which Welsh writer and TV producer's credits include 'Dr Who', 'Torchwood', 'Queer as Folk', and 'Casanova'?

8. Which Welsh actor's roles have included David Frost, Tony Blair, and Brian Clough?

9. True or false – Mount Everest is named after a Welshman?

10. Which Welsh football team plays its home games at the Racecourse Ground?

11. 'Crazy Chick' was the only UK top five hit for which Welsh singer?

12. Which Welsh town was awarded city status as part of the Queen's diamond jubilee celebrations?

13. Wales is home to three National Parks. Name them.

14. The cult 1960s TV show 'The Prisoner' was filmed in which Welsh resort?

15. The world's largest literary prize for young writers is named after which writer and poet, who was born in Swansea in 1914?

MEDIUM

16. Which instrument is regarded as the national instrument of Wales?

17. The ceremony where Charles Windsor was made the Prince of Wales was held at which Welsh castle?

18. Which festival was by described former US president Bill Clinton as 'Woodstock of the mind'?

19. Approximately what percentage of the Welsh population speaks Welsh?
    a) 5%
    b) 10%
    c) 20%

20. What is the name of the peninsula that projects into the Bristol Channel in south-west Wales?
    a) Gatting Peninsula
    b) Gooch Peninsula
    c) Gower Peninsula

MEDIUM

# Quiz 99: Pot Luck

1. Percy Gibson is the husband of which veteran screen star?

2. Athlete Phillips Idowu won World Championship gold in 2009 in which field event?

3. Which 'Shooting Stars' regular won 'Celebrity Big Brother' in 2001?

4. Which Spice Girl recorded the 2012 album 'Stages'?

5. St Mary Mead is the home village of which fictional detective?

6. Which fruit gives Earl Grey tea its distinctive flavour?

7. What was the last James Bond film that starred Roger Moore as 007?

8. Van Rijn is the surname of which famous 17th-century Dutch painter?

9. Which pair of brothers were members of the Labour Cabinet from 2007 until 2010?

10. Which British artist, who died in 2008, was noted for her comic representations of plump people?

11. What is the name of the wife of former British prime minister John Major?

12. The Four Noble Truths are the central doctrine of which religion?

13. Haile Selassie was the emperor of which country?

14. The real first name of biologist Richard Dawkins is also the surname of a US President. Which one?

15. Henry VIII was the father of which three English monarchs?

16. Who was the emperor of Japan from 1926 until 1989?

17. British jazz musician Sir Johnny Dankworth was associated with which instrument?

18. What is the first name of the British composer Delius?

19. In which sport are Owen Farrell, Toby Flood, and Billy Twelvetrees notable performers?

20. Complete the title of a 2012 BBC drama: 'Last Tango in ...'
    a) Burnley
    b) Halifax
    c) Rotherham

## Answers to Quiz 98: Wales

1. Seaweed
2. Rhodri Morgan
3. Menai Bridge
4. Timothy Dalton
5. Chepstow
6. Brecon
7. Russell T Davies
8. Michael Sheen
9. True
10. Wrexham
11. Charlotte Church
12. St Asaph
13. Snowdonia, Pembrokeshire Coast, and the Brecon Beacons
14. Portmeirion
15. Dylan Thomas
16. Harp
17. Caernarfon Castle
18. The Hay Festival of Literature
19. 20%
20. Gower Peninsula

# Quiz 100: Famous Johns

Identify the famous Johns from the clues below:

1. Played Jack Sparrow in the 'Pirates of the Caribbean' films.

2. The first non-British player to win the World Darts Championship.

3. Novelist whose works include 'East of Eden' and 'Cannery Row'.

4. Politician who was the second president of the USA.

5. The only England player named in the 2006 FIFA World Cup all-star squad.

6. Character played on TV by George Peppard and in film by Liam Neeson.

7. Played film producer John Chambers in the 2012 film 'Argo'.

8. Actor who briefly played Scottish detective Inspector Rebus.

9. Prime minister of Australia from 1996 to 2007.

10. Succeeded Hillary Clinton as US Secretary of State.

11. Clergyman beatified by Pope Benedict XVI on his 2010 visit to Britain.

12. The BBC's cricket correspondent.

13. Architect best known for designing Blenheim Palace.

14. Broadcaster whose real name was John Ravenscroft.

15. The first darts player to throw a televised nine-dart finish.

16. Welsh rugby player, nicknamed 'The King', who retired in 1972 at the age of just 27.

17. The real name of Sex Pistols' frontman Johnny Rotten.

18. Emmy-award-winning American actor who played Arthur Mitchell in 'Dexter' and provided the voice of Lord Farquaad in 'Shrek'.

19. Glasgow-born actor who played Dr Jack Harkness in 'Torchwood'.

20. Band whose biggest hit was 'Shattered Dreams'.

**MEDIUM**

## Answers to Quiz 99: Pot Luck

1. Joan Collins
2. Triple jump
3. Jack Dee
4. Melanie C
5. Miss Marple
6. Bergamot orange
7. A View to a Kill
8. Rembrandt
9. Ed and David Miliband
10. Beryl Cook
11. Norma
12. Buddhism
13. Ethiopia
14. Clinton
15. Edward VI, Elizabeth I, Mary I
16. Hirohito
17. Saxophone
18. Frederick
19. Rugby union
20. Halifax

# Quiz 101: Pot Luck

1. The Golden Temple in Amritsar is an important pilgrimage site for followers of which religion?

2. Which instrument is the lowest-pitched member of the violin family?

3. What name is shared by an 18th-century British landscape painter and the actor who plays Gaius in the TV drama 'Merlin'?

4. What are the three European countries that are members of the Commonwealth?

5. Which American architect's buildings include the Imperial Hotel in Tokyo and the Guggenheim Museum in New York?

6. Who are the five permanent members of the UN Security Council?

7. In 2009, Jacob Zuma was elected president of which country?

8. Whose 2013 funeral was given the code name 'True Blue'?

9. Which Irish band takes its name from an epic poem by Dante Alighieri?

10. Which jockey has won The Derby the most times?

11. Which bird gives its name to a score of two under par for a hole in golf?

12. Crooner Engelbert Humperdinck and indie rockers Kasabian are from which British city?

13. What does the acronym DINKY stand for?

14. What weather-related phenomenon is also the nickname of Spanish golfer Sergio Garcia?

15. Tempura is a common dish in the cuisine of which country?

16. Who was the first woman to be elected Speaker of the House of Commons?

17. The detective drama 'Dalziel and Pascoe' was set in which English county?

18. Who sang the theme song to the 1995 James Bond film 'Goldeneye'?

19. What is the currency of Lebanon and Syria?
    a) dollar
    b) lira
    c) pound

20. Ed Miliband is an MP for which Yorkshire town?
    a) Doncaster
    b) Rotherham
    c) Wakefield

MEDIUM

## Answers to Quiz 100. Famous Johns

1. Johnny Depp
2. John Part
3. John Steinbeck
4. John Adams
5. John Terry
6. John 'Hannibal' Smith
7. John Goodman
8. John Hannah
9. John Howard
10. John Kerry
11. Cardinal John Henry Newman
12. Jonathan Agnew
13. John Vanbrugh
14. John Peel
15. John Lowe
16. Barry John
17. John Lydon
18. John Lithgow
19. John Barrowman
20. Johnny Hates Jazz

# Quiz 102: Mary, Mary

Identify the famous Marys from the clues below:

1. American soul singer who partnered U2 on the 2006 number two single 'One'.

2. Became Ireland's first female president in 1990.

3. Retail expert who was appointed by David Cameron to conduct a review of the British High Street.

4. According to the gospels of Mark and John, the first person to see Jesus after the resurrection.

5. English author who created the fictional character 'Frankenstein'.

6. Railway station on the Monopoly board.

7. Social activist who was the first president of the National Viewers' and Listeners' Association?

8. Best-selling American thriller writer whose books include 'I Heard That Song Before', 'Where Are You Now', and 'Just Take My Heart'.

9. Fictional nanny of the Banks family.

10. In 1997, she became Ireland's second female president.

11. Founder of the Christian Science religious movement.

12. Welsh singer who topped the charts in 1968 with 'Those Were the Days'.

13. Eighteenth-century writer and philosopher who wrote 'A Vindication of the Rights of Woman'.

14. Athlete who won gold in the pentathlon at the 1972 Olympic Games.

Answers – page 209

15. Jamaican nurse who cared for British soldiers at the front during the Crimean War.

16. Silent movie star who was known as America's Sweetheart.

17. Cambridge University professor described as 'Britain's best known classicist'.

18. American athlete who tripped and fell after a controversial collision with Zola Budd in the 3000m at the 1984 Olympics.

19. ITV newsreader who also presents the TV cooking show 'Britain's Best Dish'.

20. French tennis player who won the Australian Open in 1995 and the French Open in 2000.

MEDIUM

## Answers to Quiz 101: Pot Luck

1. Sikhism
2. Double bass
3. Richard Wilson
4. Cyprus, Malta, and the United Kingdom
5. Frank Lloyd Wright
6. China, France, Russia, UK, and USA
7. South Africa
8. Margaret Thatcher
9. The Divine Comedy
10. Lester Piggott
11. Eagle
12. Leicester
13. Double Income No Kids Yet
14. El Niño
15. Japan
16. Betty Boothroyd
17. Yorkshire
18. Tina Turner
19. Pound
20. Doncaster

# Quiz 103: Pot Luck

1. Robert De Niro put on almost 4 stone in weight while portraying Jake La Motta in which film?

2. The WTA and ATP are governing bodies in which sport?

3. Which reggae artist recorded the 1977 album 'Exodus'?

4. The Battle of Hamburger Hill was fought in which war?

5. Who are the two jockeys to have been team captains on TV quiz show 'A Question of Sport'?

6. The TV drama 'Broadchurch' is set in which English county?

7. The 1993 film 'Jurassic Park' was based on a novel by which author?

8. Marlo Stanfield, Avon Barksdale, and Ervin Burrell were characters in which acclaimed American drama?

9. Which music impresario is the founder of a company called The Really Useful Group?

10. Bing Crosby's best-selling festive song 'White Christmas' appeared in which 1942 film?

11. In 1974, which politician said, 'It will be years – and not in my time – before a woman will lead the party or become prime minister'?

12. 'Two Jags' was the nickname of which British politician?

13. What is the slowest of the four Olympic swimming strokes?

14. 'We'll take a quick bite in the Restaurant at the End of the Universe' is the closing line of which cult science-fiction comic novel?

15. John Wheeley Lea and William Henry Perrins invented which popular condiment?

16. Annie Elizabeth, Egremont Russet, and Laxton's Superb are varieties of which fruit?

17. Longleat Safari Park is in which English county?

18. What is the first name of the fictional detective Taggart?

19. Who is the owner of the award-winning London restaurant Le Gavroche?
    a) Heston Blumenthal
    b) Gordon Ramsay
    c) Michel Roux Jr

20. What is the distance of the longest indoor swimming race at the Olympic Games?
    a) 800m
    b) 1,000m
    c) 1,500m

MEDIUM

## Answers to Quiz 102: Mary, Mary

1. Mary J Blige
2. Mary Robinson
3. Mary Portas
4. Mary Magdalene
5. Mary Shelley
6. Marylebone
7. Mary Whitehouse
8. Mary Higgins Clark
9. Mary Poppins
10. Mary McAleese
11. Mary Baker Eddy
12. Mary Hopkin
13. Mary Wollstonecraft
14. Mary Peters
15. Mary Seacole
16. Mary Pickford
17. Mary Beard
18. Mary Decker
19. Mary Nightingale
20. Mary Pierce

# Quiz 104: Night and Day

1. 'The Next Day' was a 2013 album by which legendary pop figure?

2. Hermia, Helena, Lysander, and Demetrius are characters in which Shakespeare play?

3. Who preceded Sir John Betjeman as Poet Laureate?

4. Timothy Dalton made his debut as James Bond in which 1987 film?

5. Which cult 1980s film starred Matthew Broderick as a high-school student who skipped school with entertaining results?

6. Billy Bleach and Tommy Cockles are characters created by which British comedian?

7. 'Ali Baba and the Forty Thieves' and 'The Seven Voyages of Sinbad the Sailor' are stories from which collection of folk tales?

8. A dungeon master called Treguard was the guide in which 1980s children's adventure TV show?

9. By what name is the plant 'Atropa belladonna' better known?

10. Which Indian-American director's films include 'The Sixth Sense', 'Unbreakable', and 'The Last Airbender'?

11. Mark Wahlberg played a character called Dirk Diggler in which 1997 film directed by Paul Thomas Anderson?

12. Welshman Ryan Day reached the quarter finals of the 2011 World Championship in which sport?

13. An alien called Klaatu is the central character in which 1951 sci-fi classic which was remade in 2008 starring Keanu Reeves?

14. Which Woody Allen romantic comedy was nominated in the Best Picture category at the 2012 Oscars?

15. The 1978 top ten hit 'Lovely Day' was recorded by which American soul singer?

16. In the TV comedy 'Friends', Joey played Dr Drake Ramoray in which US medical soap?

17. Signed in 1995, what set of accords brought the Bosnian War to an end?

18. What was the name of the 2004 film that later became a TV series based on an American high-school football team in Texas?

19. In 1994 Bon Jovi reached number 4 in the charts with a song called 'Midnight in ...?'
    a) Chelsea  b) Fulham  c) West Ham

20. What was the title of a 2009 film starring Zooey Deschanel and Joseph Gordon-Levitt?
    a) (300) Days of Summer  b) (400) Days of Summer
    c) (500) Days of Summer

MEDIUM

## Answers to Quiz 103: Pot Luck

1. Raging Bull
2. Tennis
3. Bob Marley
4. Vietnam War
5. Willie Carson and Frankie Dettori
6. Dorset
7. Michael Crichton
8. The Wire
9. Andrew Lloyd-Webber
10. Holiday Inn
11. Margaret Thatcher
12. John Prescott
13. Breaststroke
14. The Hitchhiker's Guide to the Galaxy
15. Worcestershire sauce
16. Apple
17. Wiltshire
18. Jim
19. Michel Roux Jr
20. 1,500m

# Quiz 105: Pot Luck

1. Who played Johnny Cash in the 2005 film biopic 'Walk the Line'?

2. Spiro Agnew and Gerald Ford served as vice-president to which US president?

3. 'My Sweet Lord' was the first solo number one hit for which Beatle?

4. In which film and TV franchise will you see fictional species called Ferengi, Betazoid, and Borg?

5. 'Hot dogs!' in the 1929 film 'The Karnival Kid' were the first words uttered by which cartoon character?

6. The main line of the Grand Union Canal starts in London and ends in which city?

7. What is the longest motorway in Britain?

8. True or false – there are villages in Norfolk called Great Snoring and Little Snoring?

9. An Eboracian is the name used to describe someone from which city?

10. 'Pablo Honey' was the debut album from which influential British rock band?

11. Swimmer Sharron Davies, diver Tom Daley, and politician Michael Foot were all born in which city?

12. Which comedian and film star said, 'I never forget a face, but in your case I'd be glad to make an exception'?

13. Town Moor is an alternative name for which Yorkshire racecourse?

14. Which famous thriller writer, best known for 'The Thirty-Nine Steps' went on to serve as the Governor General of Canada?

15. Which British actor and comedian committed suicide in Sydney, Australia on 24 June 1968?

16. What colour are Scottish £50 notes?

17. The port cities of Sevastopol and Odessa are in which European country?

18. The 1356 Battle of Poitiers was fought during which war?

19. In a game of cricket, what is the most common way for a batsman to be dismissed?
a) bowled  b) caught  c) leg before wicket

20. Carl Menger, Eugen von Böhm-Bawerk, and Friedrich von Wieser were associated with which school of economics?
a) Austrian School  b) German School  c) Swiss School

**MEDIUM**

## Answers to Quiz 104: Night and Day

1. David Bowie
2. A Midsummer Night's Dream
3. Cecil Day-Lewis
4. The Living Daylights
5. Ferris Bueller's Day Off
6. Simon Day
7. The Thousand and One Nights
8. Knightmare
9. Deadly Nightshade
10. M Night Shyamalan
11. Boogie Nights
12. Snooker
13. The Day the Earth Stood Still
14. Midnight in Paris
15. Bill Withers
16. Days of Our Lives
17. Dayton Accords
18. Friday Night Lights
19. Chelsea
20. (500) Days of Summer

# Quiz 106: TV Comedies

MEDIUM

1. Which character made his first TV appearance in 10 years for Comic Relief 2013?

2. Who was the original host of comedy quiz show 'Never Mind the Buzzcocks'?

3. Who played cleaner Barbara Petrietskivadorski in the BBC1 sitcom 'Not Going Out'?

4. 'Rock and Chips' was the prequel to which TV comedy?

5. Oil Drum Lane was the setting for which classic comedy?

6. Which TV comedy was set in the fictional town of Royston Vasey?

7. Which comedian is the creator and host of TV's 'Comedy Vehicle'?

8. What is the name of the teacher played by Greg Davies in 'The Inbetweeners'?

9. 'The Thick of It' is set in which fictional government department?

10. Richard Briers played Martin Bryce in which 1980s sitcom?

11. Daisy Steiner and Tim Bisley were the central characters in which Channel 4 comedy?

12. What is the name of the comic-book-store owner in 'The Big Bang Theory'?

13. Which member of the Monty Python team was originally asked to host the panel show 'QI'?

14. The mockumentary 'Life's Too Short' starred which actor?

15. Ralph Bates played the title character in which 1980s sitcom set in a singles club?

16. What is the occupation of the the character played by Sue Perkins in 'Heading Out'?

17. Starring Jo Brand and Vicki Pepperdine, 'Getting On' is set in what type of establishment?

18. Neil Patrick Harris from 'How I Met Your Mother' found fame playing which teenage doctor?

19. Comedy duo 'Flight of the Conchords' are from which country?
    a) Australia
    b) New Zealand
    c) South Africa

20. 'Phoenix Nights' was set in which northern town?
    a) Blackburn
    b) Bolton
    c) Burnley

MEDIUM

## Answers to Quiz 105: Pot Luck

1. Joaquin Phoenix
2. Richard Nixon
3. George Harrison
4. Star Trek
5. Mickey Mouse
6. Birmingham
7. M6
8. True
9. York
10. Radiohead
11. Plymouth
12. Groucho Marx
13. Doncaster
14. John Buchan
15. Tony Hancock
16. Green
17. Ukraine
18. The Hundred Years' War
19. Caught
20. Austrian School

# Quiz 107: Pot Luck

1. Who was the US vice-president from 1981 until 1989?

2. What name is shared by a former England rugby union captain and a celebrity chef?

3. Which comedian, who died in 2013, was best known for his 'broken microphone' routine?

4. Which politician was injured in a plane crash during the 2010 general election campaign?

5. Which animated duo made their big-screen debut in the 1940 film 'Puss Gets the Boot'?

6. 'Autobahn' and 'The Man-Machine' were the only UK top ten albums by which influential electronic band?

7. Which German city provided the title of a 2005 film directed by Steven Spielberg?

8. Who was the first, and so far only, British driver to win the Formula One Drivers' Championship three times?

9. The flag of St Piran is an emblem of which part of the UK?

10. Which famous racehorse won the Cheltenham Gold Cup in 1964, 1965, and 1966?

11. The original 'CSI: Crime Scene Investigation' TV series is set in which city?

12. Ethiopian Tsegaye Kebede and Kenyan Priscah Jeptoo were the 2013 winners of which annual sporting event?

13. 'The Potato Eaters', 'Irises', and 'Wheatfield with Crows' are works by which Dutch painter?

14. Who is older – Scarlett Johansson or Reese Witherspoon?

15. Which member of the royal family owns a share in a race horse called Usain Colt?

16. What is the only US state that ends with the letter G?

17. What nationality is the action-movie star Dolph Lundgren?

18. The Wanamaker Trophy is awarded to the winner of which of golf's four majors?

19. Which team won the first ever Cricket World Cup?
    a) England
    b) South Africa
    c) West Indies

20. What is the name of the home ground of Birmingham City FC?
    a) St Andrew's
    b) St David's
    c) St George's

## Answers to Quiz 106: TV Comedies

1. David Brent
2. Mark Lamarr
3. Miranda Hart
4. Only Fools and Horses
5. Steptoe and Son
6. The League of Gentlemen
7. Stewart Lee
8. Mr Gilbert
9. Department of Social Affairs and Citizenship (DoSAC)
10. Ever Decreasing Circles
11. Spaced
12. Stuart
13. Michael Palin
14. Warwick Davis
15. Dear John
16. Vet
17. Hospital
18. Doogie Howser MD
19. New Zealand
20. Bolton

# Quiz 108: Europe

MEDIUM

1. Noted for its prehistoric cave paintings, the Altamira cave is in which country?

2. Transylvania is a region of which European country?

3. Heligoland is an island territory belonging to which country?

4. What is the longest river in Europe?

5. Metalist Kharkiv and Dnipro Dnipropetrovsk are football teams from which country?

6. The Palio horse festival takes place in which Italian city?

7. If you flew due east from Edinburgh, which country would you next reach?

8. Ajaccio is the capital city of which Mediterranean island?

9. The musical acts Air, MC Solaar and M83 are from which country?

10. De Telegraaf and De Volksrant are newspapers published in which major European city?

11. Bergen is the second largest city of which country?

12. The 'Vuelta' is a major cycle race in which European country?

13. Which Scandinavian country is not a member of the European Union?

14. Scene of a massive nuclear accident in 1986, Chernobyl is in which country?

15. Which country is referred to by the initials FYROM?

Answers – page 221

16. Car manufacturer Skoda is based in which country?

17. Sir Simon Rattle is the principal conductor of which European orchestra?

18. The Faroe Islands are a self-governing administrative division of which country?

19. Which is the most northerly of the Spanish Costas?
    a) Costa Blanca
    b) Costa Brava
    c) Costa del Sol

20. Which is the most northerly of the following capital cities?
    a) Berlin
    b) Brussels
    c) Paris

**MEDIUM**

## Answers to Quiz 107: Pot Luck

1. George HW Bush
2. Phil Vickery
3. Norman Collier
4. Nigel Farage
5. Tom and Jerry
6. Kraftwerk
7. Munich
8. Jackie Stewart
9. Cornwall
10. Arkle
11. Las Vegas
12. The London Marathon
13. Vincent van Gogh
14. Reese Witherspoon
15. Prince Harry
16. Wyoming
17. Swedish
18. US PGA Championship
19. West Indies
20. St Andrew's

# Quiz 109: Pot Luck

1. The Arlington National Cemetery is in which US state?

2. Football club Anderlecht is based in which European capital city?

3. Ole Kirk Christiansen was the founder of which toy company?

4. Which actor, who left the country in 2012 said, 'France is sad and I think that the French are fed up'?

5. Former US president Bill Clinton's middle name is also the surname of another former US president. Which one?

6. What sort of creatures live in a nest called a formicary?

7. Which two countries occupy the Caribbean island of Hispaniola?

8. Which actor played Captain Peacock in 'Are You Being Served?' and Truly in 'Last of the Summer Wine'?

9. The most easterly point of England is in which county?

10. Which British driver won his only Formula One Drivers' Championship crown in 1996?

11. The flag of the Bahamas is made up of which three colours?

12. Tarom is the national airline of which European country?

13. Recorded in 1949 and 1950, 'The Birth of Cool' is a classic album by which jazz musician?

14. Which unaccompanied singing style translates into English as 'in the church style'?

15. By what name is the comedian Louis Szekely better known?

16. 'Impression, Sunrise' and 'Beach in Pourville' are paintings by which French artist?

17. Which note is traditionally used for tuning musical instruments?

18. In which city will you find a famous sporting venue called Croke Park?

19. Complete the title of a famous sculpture by Rodin: 'The Burghers of ...'
    a) Boulogne
    b) Calais
    c) Dieppe

20. Which former British prime minister also conducted the London Symphony Orchestra?
    a) Ted Heath
    b) John Major
    c) Margaret Thatcher

## Answers to Quiz 108: Europe

1. Spain
2. Romania
3. Germany
4. The Volga
5. Ukraine
6. Siena
7. Denmark
8. Corsica
9. France
10. Amsterdam
11. Norway
12. Spain
13. Norway
14. Ukraine
15. Former Yugoslav Republic of Macedonia
16. Czech Republic
17. Berlin Philharmonic
18. Denmark
19. Costa Brava
20. Berlin

MEDIUM

# Quiz 110: Starts with the Same Letter

1. Which actress played Dr Watson in a modern-day reworking of the Sherlock Holmes stories?

2. Which actor plays Brian Lane in the detective drama 'New Tricks'?

3. Which American composer wrote the opera 'Porgy and Bess'?

4. Dave Grohl is the lead singer with which rock group?

5. Which singer-songwriter is known as the 'Bard of Barking'?

6. By what collective name are the comic-book superheroes the Thing, Mister Fantastic, the Invisible Woman, and the Human Torch known?

7. Which Canadian comic actor is best known for playing international man of mystery Austin Powers?

8. 'The Big Easy' is the nickname of which golfer?

9. Which moustachioed England batsman scored 333 in a Test match against India in 1990?

10. 'Goody Two Shoes' was a number one hit in 1982 for which British singer?

11. Who was the subject of a 1992 biopic starring Robert Downey Jr and directed by Richard Attenborough?

12. 'Duel' was the first feature-length film made by which director?

13. Who held the world record in the long jump from 1968 until 1991?

14. What was the name of the character played by Leonard Rossiter in the TV comedy 'Rising Damp'?

15. Which actor played Fox Mulder in the TV drama 'The X Files'?

16. The Aldeburgh Festival was founded by which composer?

17. Which footballer was voted FIFA World Player of the Year in 1998, 2000, and 2003?

18. What was the name of the detective played by Humphrey Bogart in the 1941 film noir 'The Maltese Falcon'?

19. Walter White is the central character in which cult American TV drama?

20. Which actor is best known for playing Arnie Vinick in 'The West Wing' and Hawkeye Pierce in 'M*A*S*H'?

MEDIUM

## Answers to Quiz 109: Pot Luck

1. Virginia
2. Brussels
3. Lego
4. Gerard Depardieu
5. Jefferson
6. Ants
7. Haiti and the Dominican Republic
8. Frank Thornton
9. Suffolk
10. Damon Hill
11. Black, yellow, and blue
12. Romania
13. Miles Davis
14. A capella
15. Louis CK
16. Claude Monet
17. A
18. Dublin
19. Calais
20. Ted Heath

# Quiz 111: Pot Luck

1. 'Il Travatore' is an opera by which composer?

2. Who is the tennis-playing wife of Andre Agassi?

3. What is the third largest planet of the Solar System?

4. Which US state is bordered by Colorado, Nebraska, Missouri and Oklahoma?

5. What natural phenomenon takes its name from the Japanese words for 'harbour' and 'wave'?

6. 'Composition with Yellow, Blue, and Red' and 'Composition II in Red, Blue, and Yellow' are works by which Dutch abstract painter?

7. Which author wrote and created the hit TV drama 'Downton Abbey'?

8. The BJP and Congress are the two main political parties in which Commonwealth country?

9. What nationality is Premier League football manager Michael Laudrup?

10. Which actor's film credits include 'Jane Eyre', 'X-Men: First Class', 'A Dangerous Method', and 'Shame'?

11. Who dragged up to play Edna Turnblad in the 2007 film version of the musical 'Hairspray'?

12. What did the F in F Scott Fitzgerald stand for?

13. In which sport do teams from Australia and New Zealand compete for the Chappell–Hadlee Trophy?

14. Eric, Tinker, Charlie Gimbert, and Lady Jane Felsham were characters in which TV drama?

Answers – page 227

15. Who played Robert Langdon in the 2006 film version of 'The Da Vinci Code'?

16. 'The Treachery of Images' is a painting by which Belgian surrealist?

17. What does the S in the acronym UNESCO stand for?

18. The WPBSA is the governing body of which sport?

19. In which game are Phil Hellmuth, Gus Hansen, and Tom Dwan notable names?
    a) chess
    b) poker
    c) pool

20. Complete the title of the 2010 film: 'How To Train Your ...'
    a) Dragon
    b) Mother-in Law
    c) Husband

**MEDIUM**

## Answers to Quiz 110: Starts with the Same Letter

| | |
|---|---|
| 1. Lucy Liu | 11. Charlie Chaplin |
| 2. Alun Armstrong | 12. Steven Spielberg |
| 3. George Gershwin | 13. Bob Beamon |
| 4. Foo Fighters | 14. Rupert Rigsby |
| 5. Billy Bragg | 15. David Duchovny |
| 6. Fantastic Four | 16. Benjamin Britten |
| 7. Mike Myers | 17. Zinedine Zidane |
| 8. Ernie Els | 18. Sam Spade |
| 9. Graham Gooch | 19. Breaking Bad |
| 10. Adam Ant | 20. Alan Alda |

# Quiz 112: Pop Music part 2

1.  Who topped the charts in the UK and the USA in 2011 with 'Grenade'?

2.  Producer and DJ David Guetta is from which country?

3.  Which medical condition was the title of a 2013 hit for Demi Lovato?

4.  Which group performed in front of over 623,000 fans during a series of seven concerts at Wembley Stadium in 2011?

5.  'Freak Like Me', 'Push the Button', and 'About You Now' were chart-topping singles by which girl group?

6.  What was The Beatles' biggest-selling album?

7.  Stewart Copeland was the drummer with which band?

8.  Which female star played the drums for a 1980s pop/dance group called The Breakfast Club?

9.  Whose 2013 world tour was called 'The Mrs Carter Show'?

10. The 2011 album 'Ceremonials' was the second studio album by which British indie band?

11. Girls Aloud topped the charts in 2004 with a cover of which song by The Pretenders?

12. 'Toxic', 'Everytime', and 'Born to Make You Happy' were chart toppers by which singer?

13. The 2013 comeback single 'Get Lucky' was a number one hit single for which French dance duo?

14. What was the biggest-selling single for The Beatles?

15. Which member of the Spice Girls has gone on to have the most solo number one singles?

Answers – page 229

16. David Evans is the real name of which member of U2?

17. Which country pop singer was born Eilleen Regina Edwards?

18. 'Pure and Simple' was a million-selling single for which reality TV show winning band?

19. Where is the T in the Park festival held?
    a) England
    b) Scotland
    c) Wales

20. What was Madonna's first UK top ten single?
    a) 'Holiday'
    b) 'Material Girl'
    c) 'Dress You Up'

MEDIUM

## Answers to Quiz 111: Pot Luck

1. Giuseppe Verdi
2. Steffi Graf
3. Neptune
4. Kansas
5. Tsunami
6. Piet Mondrian
7. Julian Fellowes
8. India
9. Danish
10. Michael Fassbender
11. John Travolta
12. Francis
13. Cricket
14. Lovejoy
15. Tom Hanks
16. Rene Magritte
17. Scientific
18. Snooker
19. Poker
20. Dragon

# **Quiz 113:** Pot Luck

1. What is the square root of 256?

2. What colour are Scottish £100 notes?

3. In which country is the car manufacturer Lexus based?

4. 'We are the 99%' is a slogan commonly used by which protest organization?

5. Which British actor played Severus Snape in the 'Harry Potter' films?

6. Scrapie is a disease that most commonly affects which animal?

7. Brigham Young was a president of which religious organization?

8. Mel Gibson played detective Martin Riggs in which film franchise?

9. 'Cerebro' is the Spanish word for which organ of the body?

10. In the 1939 film 'The Wizard of Oz', what colour skin did the Wicked Witch of the West have?

11. Who is the longest-serving Labour MP in history?

12. Who played the title character in the 2013 film adaptation of 'The Great Gatsby'?

13. Which football team plays its home matches at the Madejski Stadium?

14. The Hallé is a symphony orchestra based in which city?

15. The 'Lanterne Rouge' is awarded to the last-place finisher in which sporting event?

16. Which comedian ended his shows with the line, 'May your God go with you'?

17. Which word is defined as 'a computer hacker whose activity is aimed at promoting a social or political cause'?

18. Marshall Eriksen, Lily Aldrin, and Barney Stinson are characters in which US sitcom?

19. Broadcaster Mariella Frostrup was born in which country?
    a) Denmark
    b) Norway
    c) Sweden

20. What is the name of Ray Winstone's actress daughter?
    a) Jaime
    b) Jenny
    c) Julie

**MEDIUM**

## Answers to Quiz 112: Pop Music part 2

1.  Bruno Mars
2.  France
3.  Heart Attack
4.  Take That
5.  Sugababes
6.  Sergeant Pepper's Lonely Hearts Club Band
7.  The Police
8.  Madonna
9.  Beyoncé
10. Florence and the Machine
11. I'll Stand By You
12. Britney Spears
13. Daft Punk
14. She Loves You
15. Geri Halliwell
16. The Edge
17. Shania Twain
18. Hear'say
19. Scotland
20. Holiday

# Quiz 114: Olympic Games

1. Dave Brailsford is a highly successful coach in which Olympic sport?

2. In which year did Sir Steve Redgrave win his first Olympic gold medal?

3. In which year did he win his last?

4. Keirin is an event in which Olympic sport?

5. Which Canadian city hosted the 2010 Winter Olympics?

6. Denise Lewis won gold at the 2000 games in which event?

7. What were the two martial arts at the 2012 games?

8. True or false – tossing the caber was once an Olympic sport?

9. In which year did British sprinter Linford Christie win gold in the men's 100m?

10. Why did the USA boycott the 1980 games in Moscow?

11. Rhona Martin led the British team to gold at the 2002 Winter Olympics in which sport?

12. Which country won the most medals at the 2012 London games?

13. What was the first Scandinavian city to host the Summer Olympics?

14. What is the opening event of an Olympic heptathlon?

15. What are the four cities starting with the letter A to have hosted the Summer Olympics?

16. Usain Bolt set the world record for the 200m at the 2008 games. Which runner's record did he beat?

17. Who partnered Andy Murray to the silver medal in the mixed doubles tennis at the 2012 games?

18. Which Italian city hosted the Winter Olympics in 2006?

19. How many gold medals did the British team win at the 1996 Olympics?
    a) none
    b) one
    c) two

20. Which colour does not appear on the Olympic flag?
    a) black
    b) brown
    c) green

MEDIUM

## Answers to Quiz 113: Pot Luck

1. 16
2. Red
3. Japan
4. Occupy
5. Alan Rickman
6. Sheep
7. Church of Jesus Christ of Latter-day Saints (Mormons)
8. Lethal Weapon
9. Brain
10. Green
11. Tony Benn
12. Leonardo DiCaprio
13. Reading
14. Manchester
15. Tour de France
16. Dave Allen
17. Hacktivist
18. How I Met Your Mother
19. Norway
20. Jaime

# Quiz 115: Pot Luck

1. The duodecimal system is a numbering system with which number as its base?

2. The 2022 World Cup will be hosted in which Asian country?

3. Griffin Park is the home ground of which London football club?

4. The Hyundai Motor Manufacturer is based in which country?

5. The Henri Delaunay Cup is awarded to the winners of which football competition?

6. Maximus Decimus Meridius is the central character in which 2000 historical film?

7. King Fahd International Airport is in which country?

8. What is the only element of the periodic table that begins with the letter X?

9. The phrase 'step up to the plate' derives from which sport?

10. What type of food is chipotle?

11. What was the only UK number one for the Eurythmics?

12. Punjab, Balochistan, and Sindh are provinces in which country?

13. What was the title of Kate Bush's only UK number one single?

14. Chan Kong-sang is the real name of which Hollywood star?

15. Who succeeded Sir Alec Douglas Home as the British prime minister?

16. 'The Real Deal' is the nickname of which heavyweight boxer?

17. In relation to the drama school, what do the initials RADA stand for?

18. Westmeath, Wexford, and Wicklow are counties in which Irish province?

19. Steven Victor Tallarico is the real name of which veteran US rock star?
    a) Steve Tyler
    b) Eddie Van Halen
    c) Gene Simmons

20. A barrel of oil is defined as being made up of how many US gallons?
    a) 32
    b) 42
    c) 52

MEDIUM

## Answers to Quiz 114: Olympic Games

1. Cycling
2. 1984
3. 2000
4. Cycling
5. Vancouver
6. Heptathlon
7. Judo and Taekwondo
8. False
9. 1992
10. In protest at the Soviet Union's invasion of Afghanistan
11. Curling
12. USA
13. Stockholm
14. 100m hurdles
15. Athens, Amsterdam, Antwerp, and Atlanta
16. Michael Johnson
17. Laura Robson
18. Turin
19. One
20. Brown

# Quiz 116: Families

MEDIUM

1. Ronnie, Roxie, Phil, Grant, and Sam are members of which soap family?

2. 'We Are Family' was a 1979 hit for which disco divas?

3. What is the name of the central family in animated TV comedy 'Family Guy'?

4. Which 1812 novel about a shipwreck was written by Johann David Wyss and turned into a 1960 Disney film starring John Mills?

5. Which brothers played for England in the 1966 World Cup final?

6. Who is the father of actor Emilio Estevez?

7. Which sitcom centres on the trials and tribulations of the Brockman family?

8. Who is the famous father of the film director Duncan Jones?

9. Which father and son won cricket's Ashes in Australia in 1986/87 and 2010/11 respectively?

10. What are the musical duo of vocalist Tunde Baiyewu and keyboardist Paul Tucker better known as?

11. Which actress, best known for her roles in 'Almost Famous' and 'Bride Wars', is the daughter of Goldie Hawn?

12. A member of which famous political family was the governor of the US state of Florida from 1999 to 2007?

13. Which England international footballer-turned-pundit is the cousin of Chelsea star Frank Lampard?

14. Which siblings are best known for writing and directing 'The Matrix', 'The Matrix Reloaded', and 'The Matrix Revolutions'?

15. Which celebrity couple are the parents of twins called Vivienne Marcheline and Knox Leon?

16. The 1968 song 'Dance to the Music' was the only UK top ten hit for which band?

17. What are the first names of the film-making Coen brothers?

18. Actress Liv Tyler is the daughter of the lead singer of which rock band?

19. Which Hollywood star first found fame in the short-lived ITV soap opera 'Families'?
    a) Jude Law
    b) Ewan McGregor
    c) Colin Firth

20. 'Running in the Family' was a hit for which 1980s band?
    a) Blow Monkeys
    b) Level 42
    c) Thompson Twins

MEDIUM

## Answers to Quiz 115: Pot Luck

1. 12
2. Qatar
3. Brentford
4. South Korea
5. European Championships
6. Gladiator
7. Saudi Arabia
8. Xenon
9. Baseball
10. Chili
11. There Must Be an Angel
12. Pakistan
13. Wuthering Heights
14. Jackie Chan
15. Harold Wilson
16. Evander Holyfield
17. Royal Academy of Dramatic Arts
18. Leinster
19. Steve Tyler
20. 42

# Quiz 117: Pot Luck

MEDIUM

1. What unit of length is precisely 1,852 metres?

2. Who was the first black player to captain the England football team?

3. A character called Claudius appears in which Shakespeare play?

4. What celestial object's name derives from the Greek word for 'wanderer'?

5. Robin Williams played inspirational teacher John Keating in which 1989 film?

6. In which country was 'Carry On' star Sid James born?

7. Who is the host of Channel 4 quiz show 'Five Minutes to a Fortune'?

8. The Boleyn Ground is the home of which London football club?

9. 'The God Delusion' was written by which noted biologist?

10. 'Endeavour' is a prequel to which detective drama?

11. The 2001 film 'Three Kings' was set during which conflict?

12. What long-running Radio 4 comedy is known as 'the antidote to panel games'?

13. Shaun Murphy and Neil Robertson are former world champions in which sport?

14. What branch of medicine deals with the problems and management of pregnancy?

15. Jazz musician Chet Baker was a noted player of what instrument?

16. The Order of the Aztec Eagle is a decoration awarded to foreigners by which country?

17. The area known as the Titanic Quarter can be found in which UK city?

18. Lesley Hornby is the real name of which 1960s icon?

19. Lorraine Pascale is best known for what type of cooking?
    a) baking
    b) rice dishes
    c) seafood

20. What nationality is singer Shania Twain?
    a) Australian
    b) Canadian
    c) New Zealander

**MEDIUM**

## Answers to Quiz 116: Families

1. The Mitchells
2. Sister Sledge
3. Griffin
4. The Swiss Family Robinson
5. Jack and Bobby Charlton
6. Martin Sheen
7. Outnumbered
8. David Bowie
9. Chris and Stuart Broad
10. Lighthouse Family
11. Kate Hudson
12. Bush (Jeb)
13. Jamie Redknapp
14. The Wachowskis
15. Brad Pitt and Angelina Jolie
16. Sly and the Family Stone
17. Joel and Ethan
18. Aerosmith
19. Jude Law
20. Level 42

# Quiz 118: Famous Peters

Identify the famous Peters from the clues below:

1. Oscar-winning director of 'The Lord of the Rings' and 'King Kong'.

2. Actress who played Cilla Battersby-Brown in the TV soap 'Coronation Street'.

3. Actor who is best known for playing TV detective Lieutenant Columbo.

4. Former presenter of TV show 'Live and Kicking' who also provided voices on the film 'Toy Story 2'.

5. Gay rights campaigner who attempted a citizen's arrest of Zimbabwean leader Robert Mugabe.

6. Anglo-Irish actor awarded an honorary Oscar in 2002.

7. England football team manager who gave David Beckham the captain's armband for the first time.

8. He was one third of the the music production team known as 'The Hit Factory'.

9. Lead singer with The Libertines and Babyshambles.

10. Actor who played the time lord in the 1960s films 'Dr Who and the Daleks' and 'Daleks – Invasion Earth: 2150AD'.

11. British actor, who died in 2011, who played Sergeant Obadiah Hakeswill in the TV series 'Sharpe'.

12. Singer who topped the charts with 'Flava', 'I Feel You', and 'Mysterious Girl'.

13. He was the first goalkeeper to score a goal in football's Premier League.

14. Hollywood figure who directed 'The Last Picture Show' and later appeared in 'The Sopranos' as Dr Elliot Kupferberg.

15. The bass player with Joy Division and New Order and part owner of the Hacienda nightclub.

16. The only player apart from Gary Lineker to score a goal for England at the 1986 World Cup.

17. Salford-born composer and conductor who was appointed Master of the Queen's Music in 2004?

18. Politician who is the grandson of former Labour cabinet minister Herbert Morrison.

19. His painting 'Massacre of the Innocents' sold at auction in 2002 for £49.5 million.

20. Award-winning American actor who plays Tyrion Lannister in TV's 'Game of Thrones'.

MEDIUM

## Answers to Quiz 117: Pot Luck

1. Nautical mile
2. Paul Ince
3. Hamlet
4. Planet
5. Dead Poets Society
6. South Africa
7. Davina McCall
8. West Ham United
9. Richard Dawkins
10. Inspector Morse
11. The Gulf War
12. I'm Sorry I Haven't A Clue
13. Snooker
14. Obstetrics
15. Trumpet
16. Mexico
17. Belfast
18. Twiggy
19. Baking
20. Canadian

# Quiz 119: Pot Luck

1. Which actress plays the title character in the TV comedy 'Stella'?

2. In which classic video game can you encounter ghosts called Blinky, Inky, Pinky, and Clyde?

3. In a game of Texas hold 'em poker, which hand is better – a straight or three of a kind?

4. Mr Freeze is an enemy of which comic-book superhero?

5. How many feet are in a mile?

6. What nationality is the Formula One driver Adrian Sutil?

7. Hallam University is in which British city?

8. Fill in the missing name to complete the sequence: Bobby Robson, _____, Terry Venables, Glenn Hoddle.

9. Which country stars duetted on the 1983 top ten hit 'Islands in the Stream'?

10. The criminal organization known as the Camorra is based in which Italian city?

11. If all the countries in the world beginning with the letter B were listed alphabetically, which one would come first?

12. And which one would be last on that list?

13. Which long-running sitcom was set in the village of Holmfirth?

14. The wine retsina originates from which country?

15. Who was the president of the USA from 1945 until 1953?

Answers – page 243

16. Which star of TV sketch show 'The Fast Show' played Mr Harry Weasley in 'Harry Potter and the Goblet of Fire'?

17. What name is given to a plant that lives for two or more years?

18. Tipperary and Waterford are counties in which province of Ireland?

19. What is the name of the home ground of Watford Football Club?
    a) Monastery Road
    b) Priory Road
    c) Vicarage Road

20. How many players can an American football team have on the pitch at any one time?
    a) 10
    b) 11
    c) 12

**MEDIUM**

## Answers to Quiz 118: Famous Peters

1. Peter Jackson
2. Wendi Peters
3. Peter Falk
4. Andi Peters
5. Peter Tatchell
6. Peter O'Toole
7. Peter Taylor
8. Pete Waterman
9. Pete Doherty
10. Peter Cushing
11. Pete Postlethwaite
12. Peter Andre
13. Peter Schmeichel
14. Peter Bogdanovich
15. Peter Hook
16. Peter Beardsley
17. Peter Maxwell Davies
18. Peter Mandelson
19. Peter Paul Rubens
20. Peter Dinklage

# Quiz 120: Old and New

1. New Street is the main railway station in which English city?

2. Which coastal US state is bordered by Massachusetts, Vermont, Maine, and the Canadian province of Quebec?

3. Boundary Park is the home ground of which English football club?

4. What musical TV show, often hosted by Bob Harris, ran on the BBC from 1971 until 1987?

5. By what name is the Central Criminal Court of England and Wales more commonly known?

6. 'It's Alright' is the theme tune to which popular British detective drama?

7. Which news organization has won 108 Pulitzer Prizes, more than any other organization?

8. What is the only South London street that appears on a Monopoly board?

9. The New Power Generation were the backing band for which musician?

10. Who wrote the 1951 novel 'The Old Man and the Sea'?

11. Which Hollywood star became the director of the Old Vic theatre in 2003?

12. Which famous building is located at 8–10, Broadway, London SW1?

13. Which actor played Sirius Black in the 'Harry Potter' films?

14. Javier Bardem played the terrifying Anton Chigurh in which award-winning 2007 film?

15. Released in 1996, 'Older' was the third studio album by which platinum-selling British pop star?

Answers – page 245

16. What is the fourth book of the Old Testament?

17. Which music publication has been published every week since March 1952?

18. 'The Old Lady of Threadneedle Street' is the nickname of which institution?

19. Which female singer had a number 5 hit single in 1980 with 'My Old Piano'?
    a) Diana Ross
    b) Dionne Warwick
    c) Barbra Streisand

20. New Road is the home ground of which English county cricket team?
    a) Derbyshire
    b) Northamptonshire
    c) Worcestershire

MEDIUM

## Answers to Quiz 119: Pot Luck

1. Ruth Jones
2. Pac-Man
3. A straight
4. Batman
5. 5280
6. German
7. Sheffield
8. Graham Taylor
9. Kenny Rogers and Dolly Parton
10. Naples
11. Bahamas
12. Burundi
13. Last of the Summer Wine
14. Greece
15. Harry S Truman
16. Mark Williams
17. Perennial
18. Munster
19. Vicarage Road
20. 11

# Quiz 121: Pot Luck

MEDIUM

1. Which TV panel show returned for a 45th series in April 2013?

2. Who played Winston Churchill in the 2010 film 'The King's Speech'?

3. Which rock band was the subject of a documentary called 'Crossfire Hurricane'?

4. On which subject will you see Liam Dutton, Ben Rich, and Alex Deakin report on British TV?

5. Which Christian festival is marked annually on 2 November?

6. Etymology is the study of what?

7. A jeroboam is a champagne bottle that is equivalent to how many standard bottles?

8. What is the name of the twofold pointed headdress worn by bishops?

9. The surname of which veteran female radio DJ is also the name of a familiar singing bird?

10. What classic horse race is run one day after the Derby?

11. How many players can an ice hockey team have on the rink at any one time?

12. 'A Delicate Truth' is the title of a 2013 novel by which spy writer?

13. Dechawat Poomjaeng and Ding Junhui are notables names in which sport?

14. Iggle Piggle, Upsy Daisy, and Makka Pakka are characters in which children's TV show?

15. What colour is sulphur at room temperature?

16. A cackle is the name used to describe a group of which animal?

17. Oaxaca, Tamaulipas, and Chihuahua are states in which country?

18. What are the two South American countries that are members of the oil-producers' organization OPEC?

19. Which politician will feature on the £5 note from 2016?
    a) Clement Attlee
    b) Winston Churchill
    c) Margaret Thatcher

20. What type of instrument is a hurdy-gurdy?
    a) brass
    b) percussion
    c) string

MEDIUM

## Answers to Quiz 120: Old and New

1. Birmingham
2. New Hampshire
3. Oldham Athletic
4. The Old Grey Whistle Test
5. The Old Bailey
6. New Tricks
7. The New York Times
8. Old Kent Road
9. Prince
10. Ernest Hemingway
11. Kevin Spacey
12. New Scotland Yard
13. Gary Oldman
14. No Country for Old Men
15. George Michael
16. Numbers
17. New Musical Express
18. The Bank of England
19. Diana Ross
20. Worcestershire

# Quiz 122: Connections

1. Kate Minola and Petruchio are the central characters in which Shakespeare play?

2. James Franco played Dr William 'Will' Rodman, in which 2011 science-fiction franchise reboot?

3. In ten-pin bowling, what term is used to denote three consecutive strikes?

4. What was the only UK top five hit single from The Baha Men?

5. The Australian city of Perth sits on which river?

6. What was the name of the 2006 film in which Steve Coogan and Rob Brydon played themselves filming an adaptation of 'Tristram Shandy'?

7. What is the nickname of Australian golfer Greg Norman?

8. Which song was the B-side to The Beatles' number one hit 'Hello, Goodbye'?

9. Which South African-born cricketer played 79 Test matches for England between 1982 and 1992?

10. Stuart Goddard is the real name of which musician who had a string of hits in the 1980s?

11. Which actor is the husband of singer-turned-actress Billie Piper?

12. By what name was the American blues musician Chester Arthur Burnett more commonly known?

13. In chemistry, which scientific unit is used to measure large quantities of very small entities such as atoms and molecules?

14. What was the name of the 1990s TV drama that starred Jimmy Nail as a country and western singer?

15. Which stand-up comedian collaborated with Stewart Lee on the TV shows 'Fist of Fun' and 'This Morning with Richard, not Judy'?

16. Which German football team, which was managed by Englishman Steve McClaren in 2010 and 2011, won its only Bundesliga title in 2008/09?

17. What was the first full-length feature film produced by Nick Park and the team at Aardman Animation?

18. What is the name of the pub in the TV soap Hollyoaks?
    a) The Dog in the Pond
    b) The Mucky Duck
    c) The George and Dragon

19. 'The Last Broadcast' and 'Some Cities' were chart-topping albums by which Manchester band?

20. What is the connection between all of the answers?

## Answers to Quiz 121: Pot Luck

| | |
|---|---|
| 1. Have I Got News For You | 11. Six |
| 2. Timothy Spall | 12. John Le Carré |
| 3. The Rolling Stones | 13. Snooker |
| 4. The weather | 14. In the Night Garden |
| 5. All Souls' Day | 15. Yellow |
| 6. Word origins | 16. Hyena |
| 7. Four | 17. Mexico |
| 8. Mitre | 18. Venezuela and Ecuador |
| 9. Nightingale | 19. Winston Churchill |
| 10. The Oaks | 20. String |

MEDIUM

# Quiz 123: Pot Luck

MEDIUM

1. Derek Hatton was a political leader in which British city?

2. Which London borough was created following the amalgamation of Bethnal Green, Stepney, and Poplar?

3. The first modern skyscraper was built in which American city?

4. What colour is natural unrefined cane sugar?

5. Which English monarch was known as the 'Hammer of the Scots'?

6. Swan Upping is an annual census to measure the number of swans living on which river?

7. Pall Mall and Northumberland Avenue are two of the three purple properties on a Monopoly board. What is the third?

8. If UN member states beginning with the letter G were listed alphabetically, which country would be first?

9. And which one would be last on that list?

10. A murder is the collective noun used to describe a group of which bird?

11. Which country beat England in the final of the 2007 Rugby World Cup?

12. Which alloy is produced using the Bessemer process?

13. The Classic horse races the 1,000 and 2,000 Guineas are run at which course?

14. Which dynasty provided England with its monarchs from 1603 until 1688?

15. Bloomfield Road is the home ground of which English football club?

16. What was presented to the USA by Frenchman Ferdinand de Lesseps in 1884?

17. Who are the three male suspects in the board game Cluedo?

18. Architect Jørn Utzon is best known for designing which iconic music venue which opened its doors in 1973?

19. Which country has the world's longest coastline?
    a) Canada
    b) Norway
    c) Russia

20. What type of creature is a skink?
    a) bird
    b) fish
    c) lizard

MEDIUM

## Answers to Quiz 122: Connections

1. The Taming of the Shrew
2. Rise of the Planet of the Apes
3. Turkey
4. Who Let the Dogs Out?
5. The Swan River
6. A Cock and Bull Story
7. The Great White Shark
8. I Am the Walrus
9. Allan Lamb
10. Adam Ant
11. Laurence Fox
12. Howlin' Wolf
13. Mole
14. Crocodile Shoes
15. Richard Herring
16. Wolfsburg
17. Chicken Run
18. The Dog in the Pond
19. Doves
20. They all feature an animal in the answer

# Quiz 124: The Name's James

Identify the famous Jameses from the clues below:

1. 'All the Lost Souls' and 'Some Kind of Trouble' were top five albums by which singer-songwriter?

2. Which actor played Tony Soprano in the hit TV show 'The Sopranos'?

3. Who is the bass player with indie favourites Blur?

4. Which golfer captained the European team in the 1999 Ryder Cup?

5. In 2011, Ryan Giggs set to the record for the most appearances in the Premier League. Whose record did he break?

6. Who received a nomination for a Best Actor Oscar in 2011 for his performance in '127 Hours'?

7. Which actor provided the voice of Darth Vader in the 'Star Wars' films?

8. Which author created the fictional detective Adam Dalgliesh?

9. Which Scottish broadcaster has read the classified football scores on BBC radio for the past 40 years?

10. Finnegans Wake was the last novel written by which author?

11. Who was the first cricketer to appear on the front cover of 'Attitude', Britain's biggest-selling gay magazine?

12. The 1971 hit 'You've Got a Friend' was which singer-songwriter's only UK top 40 single?

13. Which US President was shot by assassin Charles J Guiteau?

14. Which world heavyweight boxing champion was the subject of the 2005 film 'Cinderella Man' starring Russell Crowe?

15. 'The Bostonians', 'The Ambassadors', and 'The Portrait of a Lady' are novels by which Anglo-American writer?

16. Which singer's only UK hit was 'I Just Want to Make Love to You'?

17. Which US president, born in 1758, issued a famous doctrine, warning to European nations against intervening in the Western Hemisphere?

18. The 1992 film 'The Last of the Mohicans' was based on a novel by which American author?

19. What was the name of the actor who played Mr Scott in the TV and film franchise 'Star Trek'?

20. 'Go Tell It on the Mountain' is a novel by which American novelist who died in 1987?

## Answers to Quiz 123: Pot Luck

1. Liverpool
2. Tower Hamlets
3. Chicago
4. Brown
5. Edward I
6. River Thames
7. Whitehall
8. Gabon
9. Guyana
10. Crow
11. South Africa
12. Steel
13. Newmarket
14. The Stuarts
15. Blackpool
16. The Statue of Liberty
17. Colonel Mustard, Professor Plum, and Reverend Green
18. The Sydney Opera House
19. Canada
20. Lizard

# Quiz 125: Pot Luck

1. What are the three member states of the United Nations that start with the letter V?

2. By what name are members of the religious organization the Society of Jesus known?

3. In which year did Richard Nixon resign as President of the United States?

4. In relation to a military cadet organization, what do the initials ATC stand for?

5. 'Louis, I think this could be the beginning of a beautiful friendship,' is the last line of which film?

6. 'The buck stops here' is a phrase associated with which US President?

7. Which American city was virtually destroyed following a massive earthquake in April 1906?

8. 'I am the very model of a modern major-general' is a song from which Gilbert and Sullivan opera?

9. Which national newspaper was launched in February 2012?

10. 'Blood and Fire' is the motto of which religious organization?

11. What are the two Ivy League universities that start with the letter C?

12. Who played the title character in the 1988 film 'Beetlejuice'?

13. The Raptors and Blue Jays are sports teams based in which North American city?

14. What colour jersey is worn by the leader of the Giro d'Italia cycle race?

Answers – page 255

15. The genre of music known as grunge originated in which American city?

16. Which British inventor created the wind-up radio?

17. Whom did Margaret Thatcher succeed as leader of the Conservative Party?

18. Who was the first footballer to receive a knighthood?

19. What was the last James Bond film that starred Pierce Brosnan as 007?
    a) Die Another Day
    b) Goldeneye
    c) The World Is Not Enough

20. In the 1970s the UK was involved in a so-called 'cod war' with which country?
    a) Iceland
    b) Norway
    c) Sweden

MEDIUM

## Answers to Quiz 124: The Name's James

1. James Blunt
2. James Gandolfini
3. Alex James
4. Mark James
5. David James
6. James Franco
7. James Earl Jones
8. PD James
9. James Alexander Gordon
10. James Joyce
11. James Anderson
12. James Taylor
13. James A Garfield
14. James J Braddock
15. Henry James
16. Etta James
17. James Monroe
18. James Fenimore Cooper
19. James Doohan
20. James Baldwin

# Quiz 126: History part 2

1. Whom did Tony Blair succeed as leader of the Labour Party?

2. Who was the first African-American to hold the post of US Secretary of State?

3. Marie Antoinette was the wife of which French monarch?

4. What was the name of the Archbishop of Canterbury's envoy who was kidnapped in Beirut in 1987?

5. Lord Nelson died at which famous naval battle?

6. Boudica was the queen of which ancient tribe?

7. Who was the first prime minister of an independent India?

8. Which French airman was the first to fly across the English Channel?

9. Marie Louise of Austria was the second wife of which military leader?

10. Which amendment to the US Constitution completed the abolition of slavery?

11. Which three countries did US President George W Bush describe as being an 'axis of evil'?

12. Which 19th-century British civil engineer designed the main drainage system for London?

13. Which of Henry VIII's wives is buried next to him at Windsor Castle?

14. 'The Big Fella' was the nickname of which Irish leader?

15. In which year did The Great Exhibition in London take place?

16. Which US president issued a pardon to former president Richard Nixon?

17. How many countries were members of the Warsaw Pact?

18. In which year did Soviet leader Josef Stalin die?

19. Cardinal John Newman was the founder of which movement?
    a) The Birmingham Movement
    b) The Cambridge Movement
    c) The Oxford Movement

20. In which year did Margaret Thatcher resign as prime minister?
    a) 1989
    b) 1990
    c) 1991

MEDIUM

# Quiz 127: Pot Luck

1. 'Nation shall speak peace unto nation' is the motto of which organization?

2. Which word describes an organism that has both male and female reproductive organs?

3. What is the volume of a standard wine bottle?

4. Astigmatism is a defect that affects which part of the body?

5. Which range of hills are sometimes described as the 'backbone of England'?

6. Gare d'Austerlitz is a major railway station in which European city?

7. Patagonia is a region of which country?

8. 'Life on a Plate' is the title of the autobiography of which TV talent show judge?

9. 'Look Back in Anger', 'The Entertainer', and 'Epitaph for George Dillon' are works by which British playwright who died in 1994?

10. Who are the three female suspects in the board game Cluedo?

11. The silver fern is the emblem of which country?

12. Campanology is the study of what?

13. 'The Brewers' is the nickname of which English Football League club?

14. What gift is traditionally given to a couple celebrating their 15th anniversary?

15. Which political leader was assassinated by Nathuram Godse?

16. Which Italian composer wrote the opera 'Tosca'?

17. The Smithsonian American Art Museum is in which city?

18. 'Barnacle Bill' is the theme tune to which long-running television programme?

19. Who was the host of TV quiz show 'Going for Gold'?
    a) Henry Kelly
    b) Lorraine Kelly
    c) Matthew Kelly

20. The autonomous North African cities of Ceuta and Melilla are territories of which country?
    a) France
    b) Portugal
    c) Spain

**MEDIUM**

## Answers to Quiz 126: History part 2

1.  John Smith
2.  Colin Powell
3.  Louis XVI
4.  Terry Waite
5.  Trafalgar
6.  Iceni
7.  Jawaharlal Nehru
8.  Louis Blériot
9.  Napoleon Bonaparte
10. 13th
11. Iran, Iraq, and North Korea
12. Sir Joseph Bazalgette
13. Jane Seymour
14. Michael Collins
15. 1851
16. Gerald Ford
17. Eight
18. 1953
19. The Oxford Movement
20. 1990

# Quiz 128: Doctors

1. Whose 1890 work 'Portrait of Dr Gachet' was sold at auction for $51m in 1990?

2. Which founder member of the Social Democratic Party was a doctor?

3. Who are the two Scottish actors to have played TV time-traveller 'Dr Who'?

4. Which of the resident 'Chasers' on TV quiz show 'The Chase' is a medical doctor?

5. Dick van Dyke played Dr Sloan in which US detective series?

6. Which politician, who resigned as Secretary of State for Defence in 2011, was a GP before entering Parliament?

7. Which doctor-turned-best-selling author, who died in 2008, wrote 'Jurassic Park', 'Disclosure', and 'Prey'?

8. Which TV doctor's catchphrase was 'I'm listening'?

9. Dr Zoidberg is a character in which animated TV series?

10. Which doctor presented the TV documentaries 'The Human Body', 'Walking with Cavemen', and 'Child of Our Time'?

11. Which American politician, known for his libertarian views, stood in the Republican presidential primary race in 2008 and 2012?

12. Dr Pulaski and Dr Crusher appeared in which TV drama?

13. Dr Tim Brabants won Olympic gold for Great Britain in 2008 in which sport?

14. Which actor played TV's Dr Cliff Huxtable in a 1980s TV comedy?

15. The frightening Dr Percival 'Perry' Ulysses Cox is one of the main characters in which medical comedy?

MEDIUM

16. Which member of the 1960s satirical revue 'Beyond the Fringe' was a medical doctor?

17. Which former Bond girl played TV's 'Dr Quinn, Medicine Woman'?

18. What is the name of the time-travelling doctor played by Christopher Lloyd in the 'Back to the Future' films?

19. Who is the archenemy of superhero group the 'Fantastic Four'?
    a) Dr Death
    b) Dr Doom
    c) Dr Evil

20. Actor Alan Fletcher is best known for playing which TV doctor?
    a) Dr Legg
    b) Dr Karl Kennedy
    c) Dr Truman

## Answers to Quiz 127: Pot Luck

1. The BBC
2. Hermaphrodite
3. 75cl
4. The eyes
5. Pennines
6. Paris
7. Argentina
8. Gregg Wallace
9. John Osborne
10. Miss Scarlett, Mrs Peacock, and Mrs White
11. New Zealand
12. Bells
13. Burton Albion
14. Crystal
15. Mahatma Gandhi
16. Puccini
17. Washington
18. Blue Peter
19. Henry Kelly
20. Spain

MEDIUM

# Quiz 129: Pot Luck

1. Hansen's disease is another name for what ailment?

2. Which actor, who died in May 2013, was best known for playing comic Ted Bovis in the sitcom 'Hi-De-Hi!'?

3. 'Dictum meum pactum' (My word is my bond) is the motto of which financial organization?

4. 'The Persistence of Memory' is a painting by which surrealist artist?

5. Who was the last Englishman to win the men's singles title at Wimbledon?

6. Which ancient Greek philosopher founded a school in Athens called the Academy?

7. Which dramatist, who died in 1994, wrote the TV dramas 'Pennies from Heaven', 'The Singing Detective', and 'Lipstick on Your Collar'?

8. Who succeeded Boris Yeltsin as president of Russia in 2000?

9. What was the first name of the French composer Ravel?

10. Which political leader was released from house arrest by the Myanmar military junta in November 2010?

11. According to superstition, if it rains on which Saint's day, it will go on to rain for a further 40 days?

12. Who inherited the US presidency following the death of Franklin D Roosevelt?

13. 'The Aeneid' is the best-known work by which Roman poet?

14. Which king, who appears in a Christmas carol, is the patron saint of the Czechs?

15. The wine Chianti comes from which region of Italy?

16. The Willis Tower (formerly Sears Tower) is in which city?

17. The sculptor Chares of Lindos created which Wonder of the Ancient World?

18. Who was the President of the United States from 1953 until 1961?

19. The alternative massage therapy reiki originated in which country?
    a) China
    b) India
    c) Japan

20. What was the first name of the cook Mrs Beeton?
    a) Isabella
    b) Rosemary
    c) Veronica

**MEDIUM**

## Answers to Quiz 128: Doctors

1. Vincent van Gogh
2. David Owen
3. Sylvester McCoy and David Tennant
4. Paul Sinha
5. Diagnosis Murder
6. Dr Liam Fox
7. Dr Michael Crichton
8. Dr Frasier Crane
9. Futurama
10. Dr Robert Winston
11. Dr Ron Paul
12. Star Trek: The Next Generation
13. Canoeing
14. Bill Cosby
15. Scrubs
16. Jonathan Miller
17. Jane Seymour
18. Doctor Emmett Lathrop Brown
19. Dr Doom
20. Dr Karl Kennedy

# Quiz 130: Television

1. Which fictional DJ starred in the 2012 comedy 'Welcome to the Places of My Life'?

2. Colin Ball is the name of which character in 'Only Fools and Horses'?

3. What are the names of the actors who play the four main characters in comedy 'Absolutely Fabulous' (they all have first names starting with the same letter).

4. What is the name of the butler played by Jim Carter in 'Downton Abbey'?

5. Since 1982 Richard Thorp has played which character in the TV soap 'Emmerdale'?

6. Which sports broadcaster did Nick Hewer succeed as the host of the TV game show 'Countdown'?

7. A piece of music called 'Drag Racer' is the theme tune to which TV sport?

8. What is the name of the character played by Anthony Cotton in the TV soap 'Coronation Street'?

9. Which darts player finished fourth in 'I'm a Celebrity ... Get Me out of Here!' in 2012?

10. In 2012, Luke Anderson won which reality TV show?

11. Michael Byrne and Rachel Mason have been head teachers at which TV school?

12. Which EastEnders rogue had an affair with Queen Vic landlady Kat Moon?

13. Which 'dragon' from the show 'Dragons' Den' also hosted 'The Intern'?

14. Which actor plays Frank Gallagher in the Channel 4 drama 'Shameless'?

15. Which American sitcom 'about nothing' has generated a mammoth $3.1 billion in repeat fees since first airing in 1989?

16. Who plays the title character in the ITV medical drama 'Monroe'?

17. By what name are the TV duo Barry and Paul Elliott better known?

18. What is the full name of the character played by Damian Lewis in US drama 'Homeland'?

19. Who partnered Sebastian Coe on an Olympic special edition of 'Who Wants to Be a Millionaire'?
    a) Steve Cram  b) Linford Christie  c) Steve Ovett

20. What is the name of the Channel 4 documentary set in a maternity ward at a Leeds hospital?
    a) One Born Every Minute  b) Push!
    c) Where's the Midwife?

MEDIUM

## Answers to Quiz 129: Pot Luck

1. Leprosy
2. Paul Shane
3. The London Stock Exchange
4. Salvador Dali
5. Fred Perry
6. Plato
7. Dennis Potter
8. Vladimir Putin
9. Maurice
10. Aung San Suu Kyi
11. St Swithin
12. Harry S Truman
13. Virgil
14. St Wenceslaus
15. Tuscany
16. Chicago
17. The Colossus of Rhodes
18. Dwight Eisenhower
19. Japan
20. Isabella

# Quiz 131: Pot Luck

1. 'The rest is silence' were the last words of which Shakespearean character?

2. French critic Louis Leroy gave which artistic movement its name after seeing a collection of paintings by Claude Monet?

3. What name is shared by a singer who had top ten hits with 'Maria', 'She Bangs', and 'Private Emotion' and the winner of series 8 of 'The Apprentice'?

4. What is the name of the prize awarded by 'Design' magazine to the worst building of the year?

5. Which organization was the unlikely winner of the 2012 Nobel Peace Prize?

6. Who played Cleopatra in the film comedy 'Carry On Cleo'?

7. 'Money', 'London Fields', and 'The Information' are novels by which British author?

8. Which dynasty ruled China from 1368 until 1644?

9. Which British naturalist wrote 'On the Origin of Species'?

10. The films 'The Constant Gardener', 'The Tailor of Panama', and 'The Russia House' were based on novels by which British author?

11. Jake the Jailbird is a character in which popular board game?

12. The UK joined the European Economic Community on the same day as which two other countries?

13. Eric Blair was the real name of which author?

14. Derek Niven van den Bogaerde was the real name of which British actor?

15. Aleppo is the largest city in which Middle Eastern country?

Answers – page 265

16. Which actress is the subject of the musical 'End of the Rainbow'?

17. 'Gelb' is the German word for which colour?

18. Who is the host of the long-running radio panel show 'Just A Minute'?

19. US singer and rapper Nicki Minaj was born in which country?
    a) Australia
    b) Britain
    c) Trinidad

20. Judd Trump and Mark Selby are notable names in which sport?
    a) darts
    b) golf
    c) snooker

MEDIUM

## Answers to Quiz 130: Television

1. Alan Partridge
2. Trigger
3. Jennifer Saunders, Joanna Lumley, Julia Sawalha, and Jane Horrocks
4. Charlie Carson
5. Alan Turner
6. Jeff Stelling
7. Snooker
8. Sean Tully
9. Eric Bristow
10. Big Brother
11. Waterloo Road
12. Derek Branning
13. Hilary Devey
14. David Threlfall
15. Seinfeld
16. James Nesbitt
17. The Chuckle Brothers
18. Nicholas Brodie
19. Steve Cram
20. One Born Every Minute

# Quiz 132: Duets

Identify the pair that sang the following duets:

1. 'Say Say Say' (1983)

2. 'Don't Let the Sun Go Down on Me' (1991)

3. 'You Got the Dirtee Love' (2010)

4. 'The Long and Winding Road / Suspicious Minds' (2002)

5. 'Something's Gotten Hold of my Heart' (1989)

6. '7 Seconds' (1994)

7. 'Uptown Top Ranking' (1978)

8. 'Dilemma' (2002)

9. 'Where the Wild Roses Grow' (1995)

10. 'Endless Love' (1995)

11. 'Unchained Melody / (There'll Be Bluebirds Over) The White Cliffs of Dover' (1995)

12. 'Don't Give Up' (1986)

13. 'I'm Your Angel' (1998)

14. 'Me Julie' (2002)

15. 'Don't Know Much' (1989)

16. 'On My Own' (1986)

17. 'Beautiful Liar' (2007)

18. 'Tonight I Celebrate My Love' (1983)

19. 'No More Tears (Enough Is Enough)' (1979)

20. 'The Boy Is Mine' (1998)

## Answers to Quiz 131: Pot Luck

1. Hamlet
2. Impressionism
3. Ricky Martin
4. The Carbuncle Cup
5. The European Union
6. Amanda Barrie
7. Martin Amis
8. Ming
9. Charles Darwin
10. John le Carré
11. Monopoly
12. Denmark and the Republic of Ireland
13. George Orwell
14. Dirk Bogarde
15. Syria
16. Judy Garland
17. Yellow
18. Nicholas Parsons
19. Trinidad
20. Snooker

# Quiz 133: Pot Luck

1.  Drake Circus is a shopping centre in which English city?

2.  What title was shared by a 1976 hit by UK funk band Heatwave and a 1997 film starring Mark Wahlberg?

3.  Iridology is a form of alternative therapy that uses which part of the body to form a diagnosis?

4.  Melanoma is a form of cancer that affects what part of the body?

5.  Which European capital will host the final of football's Champions League in 2015?

6.  Carol Vorderman, Andrea McLean, Janet Street-Porter, and Lisa Maxwell are regulars on which lunchtime TV show?

7.  The Winter Palace is in which European city?

8.  Steven Spielberg received his first Best Director Oscar nomination for which film?

9.  The Pushkin Museum of Fine Arts is in which European city?

10. What do the initials HIV stand for?

11. 'The Time Warp' is a song from which West End musical?

12. Lauren Pope and Lauren Goodger appear in which reality TV show?

13. The Althing is the parliament of which country?

14. The Rose Bowl is the home ground of which English county cricket team?

15. Which heavyweight boxing champion is a member of parliament in Ukraine?

16. Which musician played Captain Edward Teague in 'Pirates of the Caribbean: At World's End'?

17. The Walker Cup is a competition in which sport?

18. 'The Jambos' is the nickname of which Scottish football team?

19. What is the maximum number of times a piece of A4 paper can be folded?
    a) six
    b) seven
    c) eight

20. What type of dish is baklava?
    a) fish
    b) pasta
    c) pastry

## Answers to Quiz 132: Duets

1. Paul McCartney and Michael Jackson
2. George Michael and Elton John
3. Dizzee Rascal and Florence and the Machine
4. Will Young and Gareth Gates
5. Marc Almond and Gene Pitney
6. Neneh Cherry and Youssou N'Dour
7. Althea and Donna
8. Nelly and Kelly Rowland
9. Nick Cave and Kylie Minogue
10. Mariah Carey and Luther Vandross
11. Robson and Jerome
12. Kate Bush and Peter Gabriel
13. Celine Dion and R Kelly
14. Shaggy and Ali G
15. Linda Ronstadt and Aaron Neville
16. Patti LaBelle and Michael McDonald
17. Beyoncé and Shakira
18. Peabo Bryson and Roberta Flack
19. Donna Summer and Barbra Streisand
20. Brandy and Monica

MEDIUM

# DIFFICULT QUIZZES

# Quiz 134: Pot Luck

1. French artist Nicolas-Jacques Conte invented which staple of the classroom?

2. In 2009, Sir John Sawers succeeded Sir John Scarlett in which role?

3. Which actor succeeded Dame Judi Dench as M in the James Bond film franchise?

4. Which country hosted football's Africa Cup of Nations in 2013?

5. 'Nemo me impune lacessit' (No one provokes me with impunity) is the motto of which order of chivalry?

6. Which American weekly magazine, first published in 1933, stopped producing a print edition in 2012?

7. What are the two London boroughs that start with the letter K?

8. Painter Pablo Picasso and actor Antonio Banderas were born in which Spanish city?

9. Eugène Poubelle introduced what to Paris?

10. Which saying, associated with William of Wykeham, is the motto of Winchester School and New College Oxford?

11. 2009 sci-fi drama 'District 9' was set in which country?

12. Which controversial columnist wrote the TV drama series 'Black Mirror'?

13. Which sport has provided the most captains for the TV quiz 'A Question of Sport'?

14. In 2004, who became the first woman to win the Pritzker Architecture Prize?

15. The painting 'Domplatz, Mailand' was sold at auction in May 2013 for $37m, the most for a painting by a living artist. Which German painter created it?

16. Which country is home to the world's largest population of wild camels?

17. Which painter said, 'I dream of painting and then I paint my dream'?

18. Which country won the Eurovision song contest for the fifth time in 2012 courtesy of a song called 'Euphoria' by Loreen?

19. What is celebrated in the UK on the first Thursday of March?
    a) World Book Day
    b) International Talk Like a Pirate Day
    c) World Food Day

20. DJ Judge Jules is the nephew of which famous chef?
    a) Gordon Ramsay
    b) Rick Stein
    c) Marco Pierre White

## Answers to Quiz 200: Pot Luck

1. The Silence of the Lambs
2. Russell Crowe
3. LL Cool J
4. Frank Cottrell Boyce
5. The Odd Couple
6. John Spencer
7. Isaac Newton
8. Dundee United
9. Janáček
10. Dublin
11. Headingley
12. Paris
13. Improvised Explosive Device
14. John Dillinger
15. Solheim Cup
16. Clancy
17. Ivanišević
18. Crawley Town
19. Sikhism
20. 30

**DIFFICULT**

# Quiz 135: Astronomy and Space

1. Rhea is the second largest moon of which planet?

2. What are Apophis, 1036 Ganymed, and 2062 Aten?

3. Excluding the planets and the sun, what is the largest body in our solar system?

4. Who was the third person to walk on the moon?

5. Which astronomer said, 'All truths are easy to understand once they are discovered; the point is to discover them'?

6. Which galaxy is generally regarded as the most distant object visible to the naked eye?

7. Which six-letter word describes the position when three celestial bodies appear to be in a straight line?

8. Launched in 2009, the largest telescope ever flown into space is named after which German-born British astronomer?

9. In relation to space, what do the initials SFEI stand for?

10. Which Shakespearean character is also the name of the largest moon of the planet Uranus?

11. Which London tube station shares its name with the nickname of the open star cluster known as the Pleiades?

12. Which is the only planet of the Solar System that is less dense than water?

13. Which Italian-born French astronomer discovered a number of Saturn's moons including Iapetus, Tethys, and Dione?

14. What sort of object is Pan-Starrs?

15. Which physicist, astronomer, and philosopher gave his name to the first US spacecraft to orbit Jupiter?

16. The Soviet probe Venera 4 was the first to visit which planet?

17. An equation that attempts to estimate the number of advanced civilizations in the Milky Way galaxy is named after which American astronomer and astrophysicist?

18. What name is shared by a former Ipswich Town and England footballer and a series of unmanned US probes sent to Mercury, Venus, and Mars?

19. Which planet of the Solar System has the longest day?
    a) Jupiter
    b) Neptune
    c) Venus

20. How many Apollo missions landed on the moon?
    a) four
    b) five
    c) six

## Answers to Quiz 134: Pot Luck

1. The pencil
2. Chief of the Secret Intelligence Service
3. Ralph Fiennes
4. South Africa
5. The Order of the Thistle
6. Newsweek
7. Kensington and Chelsea and Kingston upon Thames
8. Malaga
9. The dustbin
10. Manners maketh man
11. South Africa
12. Charlie Brooker
13. Rugby union – Matt Dawson, Bill Beaumont, Gareth Edwards, and Cliff Morgan
14. Zaha Hadid
15. Gerhard Richter
16. Australia
17. Vincent van Gogh
18. Sweden
19. World Book Day
20. Rick Stein

DIFFICULT

# Quiz 136: Pot Luck

1. The title of the classic Ealing comedy 'Kind Hearts and Coronets' derives from a work by which poet?

2. Which Roman soldier and statesman, who was Governor of Britain from 78AD to 85AD, was the subject of a biography by the historian Tacitus?

3. What does a palynologist study?

4. Which team beat the San Francisco 49ers to win the Super Bowl in February 2013?

5. After Stockholm and Gothenburg, what is the third largest city in Sweden?

6. Esala Perahera is an annual festival that takes place in which Asian country?

7. Which artist, born in 1599 in Spain and noted for his portraits of the Spanish royal family, said, 'I would rather be the first painter of common things than second in higher art'?

8. What rank in the RAF is equivalent to Commander in the Royal Navy and Lieutenant-Colonel in the British Army?

9. Who are the six British monarchs to have reigned for at least 50 years?

10. Which singer was the first winner of TV talent show 'Britain's Got Talent'?

11. The nationalized bank Northern Rock was bought for £747m by which financial institution in 2011?

12. The most easterly point of mainland Africa is in which country?

13. Who was the subject of a hugely popular 2011 exhibition at the National Gallery titled 'Painter at the Court of Milan'?

14. The 2012 Eurovision Song Contest was hosted in the capital city of which former Soviet Republic?

15. Which 18th-century Scottish philosopher said, 'Reason is, and ought only to be, the slave of the passions'?

16. Who was the first Irish prime minister to address members of both houses of the British parliament?

17. Who was named 'Time' magazine's Person of the Year in December 2012?

18. Which former Soviet leader has also won a Grammy award?

19. What nationality is Andris Nelsons, the conductor of the City of Birmingham Symphony Orchestra?
    a) Estonia
    b) Latvian
    c) Lithuanian

20. What was the most popular boys' baby name in 2012?
    a) Edward
    b) Harry
    c) William

## Answers to Quiz 135: Astronomy and Space

1. Saturn
2. Asteroids
3. Ganymede (moon of Jupiter)
4. Charles P 'Pete' Conrad
5. Galileo Galilei
6. Andromeda
7. Syzygy
8. William Herschel
9. Search for extraterrestrial intelligence
10. Titania
11. Seven Sisters
12. Saturn
13. Gian Cassini
14. A comet
15. Galileo
16. Venus
17. Frank Drake
18. Mariner
19. Venus
20. Six

DIFFICULT

# Quiz 137: England

1. In 2012, which city became the first in England to be named a UNESCO City of Literature?

2. Which Surrey track was the world's oldest purpose-built motor-racing circuit?

3. What famous thoroughfare was named after a former soldier and diplomat who was MP for Morpeth from 1660 to 1684?

4. Which Midlands towns were the Five Boroughs of Danelaw?

5. 'Brandy Nan' was the nickname of which English queen?

6. Which northern English city was named the happiest place in Britain in 2012?

7. The final UEFA Cup Winners' Cup final took place in 1999 in which English city?

8. The city of Lincoln stands on which river?

9. Which Yorkshire coastal town is home to a twice-yearly Goth festival?

10. Which English city hosts the annual British Fireworks Championship?

11. The English National Football Centre, St George's Park, is in which Midlands town?

12. Wulfrun Hall and the Slade Rooms are venues in which English city?

13. In which English city will you find the Royal Armouries Museum, Kirkstall Abbey, and the Henry Moore Gallery?

14. Opened in 1991, what is the most easterly bridge over the River Thames in London?

15. Which major English port city is situated between the mouths of the Test and Itchen rivers?

Answers – page 281

16. Which English county is home to the most listed buildings?

17. The Jerwood Gallery is in which south coast town?

18. Named after playwright Christopher Marlowe, who was born and raised there, the Marlowe Theatre is in which English city?

19. To the nearest million, what was the population of England according to the 2011 census?
    a) 53m
    b) 54m
    c) 55m

20. What is the surface area of England?
    a) 40,301 sq miles
    b) 50,301 sq miles
    c) 60,301 sq miles

## Answers to Quiz 136: Pot Luck

1. Tennyson
2. Agricola
3. Spores and pollen (often from fossils)
4. Baltimore Ravens
5. Malmö
6. Sri Lanka
7. Diego Velazquez
8. Wing Commander
9. Elizabeth II, Victoria, George III, Henry III, Edward III, James VI of Scotland (James I of England)
10. Paul Potts
11. Virgin Money
12. Somalia
13. Leonardo da Vinci
14. Azerbaijan
15. David Hume
16. Bertie Ahern
17. Barack Obama
18. Mikhail Gorbachev
19. Latvian
20. Harry

DIFFICULT

# Quiz 138: Pot Luck

1. The 2013 film 'Life of Pi' is based on a novel by which Canadian author?

2. On which island was footballer Cristiano Ronaldo born?

3. According to Shakespeare's Hamlet, what 'doth make cowards of us all'?

4. Every March a doll festival called Hinamatsuri is celebrated in which country?

5. Founded by King Edward VII, which order of chivalry is awarded to individuals for great achievement in the fields of the arts, learning, literature, and science?

6. Who was the last woman to win the Oscar for Best Actress who appeared in a film that also won Best Picture?

7. Britons Etienne Stott and Tim Baillie won gold at the 2012 Olympics in which sport?

8. The headquarters of the Arab League is in which city?

9. The Royal Society Winton Prize is awarded to the best book of the year written on which subject?

10. Who was the last woman to win the BBC Sports Personality of the Year award?

11. In 2012 Aidan and Joseph O'Brien became the first father and son combination to win which sporting event?

12. Laurent Gbagbo, the first former head of state to stand trial at the International Criminal Court, is the former president of which African country?

13. What is the name of the British dog show, run by the Kennel Club, exclusively for cross-bred and mongrel dogs?

14. How many member states make up the United Nations?

Answers – page 283

15. Stargardt's macular dystrophy is a disease affecting which part of the body?

16. What was the name of the oil rig in the Gulf of Mexico that exploded and sank in 2010 causing one of the biggest oil spills in history?

17. Ayutthaya, home to one of the world's largest seated images of Buddha, is in which country?

18. Pico da Neblina is the highest point of which South American country?

19. In addition to the UK, the Queen is the head of state of how many Commonwealth realms?
a) 10  b) 15  c) 20

20. In which field is Don McCullin a notable practitioner?
a) architecture  b) photography  c) sculpture

## Answers to Quiz 137: England

1. Norwich
2. Brooklands
3. Downing Street
4. Derby, Leicester, Lincoln, Nottingham, and Stamford
5. Queen Anne
6. Carlisle
7. Birmingham
8. Witham
9. Whitby
10. Plymouth
11. Burton upon Trent
12. Wolverhampton
13. Leeds
14. Queen Elizabeth II Bridge
15. Southampton
16. Devon
17. Hastings
18. Canterbury
19. 53m
20. 50,301 sq miles

DIFFICULT

# Quiz 139: Books

1. With 12m copies produced, which work of fiction had the highest initial print run in the world?

2. 'Coming Back to Me' is the title of an award-winning autobiography by which former England cricketer?

3. Complete the title of a novel by Hans Fallada: 'Alone in ...'

4. Which rugby player-turned-commentator wrote 'Beware of the Dog: Rugby's Hardman Reveals All'?

5. Which Scandinavian author created the fictional journalist Mikael Blomkvist?

6. In 2013 which British author was chosen by the estate of PG Wodehouse to write a new 'Jeeves and Wooster' novel?

7. The character of spymaster George Smiley first appeared in which novel by John Le Carré?

8. In publishing, for what is the Diagram Prize awarded?

9. Augusta Aloysius were the middle names of which influential writer?

10. Jim Grant is the real name of which best-selling British thriller writer whose works include '61 Hours' and 'A Wanted Man'?

11. 'The Love of The Last Tycoon: A Western' is an unfinished novel by which American author?

12. Which British author, who was born in Persia in 1919, was awarded the Nobel Prize for Literature in 2007?

13. Which author, who won the 1990 Booker Prize with 'Possession', said after winning that she now had the money to build her 'longed-for swimming pool in Provence'?

14. 'Mockingjay' is the third book in which science-fiction trilogy?

15. 'All the best stories are true' is the motto for which literary award, whose previous winners include Anthony Beevor, Anna Funder, and Wade Davis?

16. Which British author's novels include 'The Autograph Man', 'On Beauty', and most recently, 'NW'?

17. Which UK bookmaker sponsors the annual Sports Book of the Year award?

18. 'A Journey' was the title of the autobiography of which British prime minister?

19. The Carnegie Medal is awarded to writers of what genre of fiction?
a) children's  b) crime  c) historical

20. How many novels comprise CS Lewis's series 'The Chronicles of Narnia'?
a) three  b) five  c) seven

## Answers to Quiz 138: Pot Luck

1. Yann Martel
2. Madeira
3. Conscience
4. Japan
5. The Order of Merit
6. Hilary Swank in Million Dollar Baby
7. Canoeing (slalom)
8. Cairo
9. Science
10. Zara Phillips
11. The Epsom Derby
12. Côte d'Ivoire
13. Scruffts
14. 193
15. The eyes
16. Deepwater Horizon
17. Thailand
18. Brazil
19. 15
20. Photography

DIFFICULT

# Quiz 140: Pot Luck

1.  In 2012, Mo Yan became the first person from which country to win the Nobel Prize in Literature?

2.  Which philosopher said, 'Ask yourself whether you are happy, and you cease to be so'?

3.  Who played the MI6 Chief of Staff in the 2012 Bond film 'Skyfall'?

4.  In 2011, Dilma Rousseff became the first female president of which country?

5.  Which Austrian symbolist painter's 1907 work, 'Portrait of Adele-Bloch Bauer I' sold for $135m in 2006?

6.  Cape Blanc, the most northerly point in Africa lies in which country?

7.  If the member states of the United Nations were listed alphabetically, which country would be second on the list?

8.  The 2009 documentary 'The September Issue' focussed on Anna Wintour, the editor of which famous American magazine?

9.  7 Race Course Road is an official residence of the prime minister of which country?

10. Creme de mure is a liqueur made with what fruit?

11. Olympic president Jacques Rogge represented his country in three Olympic Games in which sport?

12. What nationality was the novelist Jorge Luis Borges?

13. William Booth was the founder and first general of which organization?

14. The skeleton of which British philosopher, complete with a wax head, is preserved and on display at University College London?

15. Covering an area of 112 square miles, what is England's smallest National Park?

16. What fruit is used in the production of the spirit 'slivovica'?

17. What is the only horse racing course in the county of Northamptonshire?

18. Which musician played Pontius Pilate in the 1993 film The Last Temptation of Christ?

19. The coronet of which rank of the peerage features eight silver balls on stalks alternating with eight gold strawberry leaves?
a) Earl  b) Duke  c) Marquis

20. What was the most popular girls' baby name in 2012?
a) Amelia  b) Catherine  c) Olivia

## Answers to Quiz 139: Books

1. Harry Potter and the Deathly Hallows
2. Marcus Trescothick
3. Berlin
4. Brian Moore
5. Stieg Larsson
6. Sebastian Faulks
7. Call for the Dead
8. The book with the oddest title of the year
9. James Joyce
10. Lee Child
11. F Scott Fitzgerald
12. Doris Lessing
13. AS Byatt
14. The Hunger Games
15. The Samuel Johnson Prize for Non-fiction
16. Zadie Smith
17. William Hill
18. Tony Blair
19. Children's
20. Seven

DIFFICULT

# Quiz 141: Films part 1

1.  Which film had actors nominated in all four acting categories at the 2013 Oscars – the first time that had happened in over 30 years?

2.  Who played both title characters in the 2012 film 'Jack and Jill'?

3.  Who are the two men to have been nominated for Best Picture as well as directing, acting, and screenwriting Oscars?

4.  Who is the youngest woman to be nominated for a Best Actress Oscar more than once?

5.  Who was the only person nominated in an acting category at the 2013 Oscars who was also nominated the year before?

6.  Which foreign-language film was nominated in the Best Picture category at the 2013 Oscars?

7.  What was the name of the villain played by Tom Hardy in 'Batman: The Dark Knight Rises'?

8.  Who played the lead role in the 2012 film 'The Bourne Legacy'?

9.  Which 86-year-old was nominated in the Best Actress category at the 2013 Oscars?

10.  Which 9-year-old was nominated in the same category at the same ceremony?

11.  Running some 234 minutes, what is the longest film to win an Oscar for Best Picture?

12.  Who received his 48th Oscar nomination in 2013?

13.  How many foreign-language films have won the Oscar for Best Picture?

14.  Which noted director played uber-villain The Zec in the 2012 film 'Jack Reacher'?

15. In 2003, who became the youngest man to win the Oscar for Best Actor?

16. Who has hosted the Oscars ceremony the most times?

17. In 1991, what became the first animated film to be nominated for a Best Picture Oscar?

18. Which musician played Inspector Good in the 1991 film 'Hook'?

19. In the Coen brothers' cult classic 'The Big Lebowski', what is Lebowski's first name?
    a) Jeffrey
    b) Kevin
    c) Norman

20. Which Australian singer-turned-actor had a cameo in the 2012 film 'Holy Motors'?
    a) Nick Cave
    b) Kylie Minogue
    c) Natalie Imbruglia

## Answers to Quiz 140: Pot Luck

1.  China
2.  JS Mill
3.  Rory Kinnear
4.  Brazil
5.  Gustav Klimt
6.  Tunisia
7.  Albania
8.  Vogue
9.  India
10. Blackberry
11. Yachting
12. Argentine
13. The Salvation Army
14. Jeremy Bentham
15. Norfolk Broads
16. Plums
17. Towcester
18. David Bowie
19. Earl
20. Amelia

DIFFICULT

# Quiz 142: Pot Luck

1. Marouane Fellaini, Eden Hazard, and Christian Benteke play international football for which country?

2. Which influential German group performed a series of sell-out gigs at Tate Modern in February 2013?

3. The 2013 film 'A Good Day to Die Hard' is largely set in which city?

4. A yellow star appears on the flag of which South American country?

5. Who played pilot Whip Whitaker in the 2012 film 'Flight'?

6. Which alcoholic drink was often referred to as 'la fée verte' (the green fairy)?

7. Who is the host of American eating-challenge programme 'Man Versus Food'?

8. The Battle of Zama in 202 BC was the last conflict of which war fought between Rome and Carthage?

9. Which cricketer did Australian captain Steve Waugh describe as 'The Don Bradman of bowling'?

10. Which artist said, 'Art is the lie that enables us to realize the truth'?

11. The equator passes through which five African countries?

12. The classic Christmas film 'Home Alone' is set in which American city?

13. 'My Animals and Other Family' is the title of the autobiography of which British broadcaster?

14. The liqueur Sambuca takes its name from which fruit?

15. What is the largest National Park in Britain?

DIFFICULT

Answers – page 291

16. Which Spain and Chelsea footballer has a degree in sports science from the University of Madrid?

17. In the sci-fi classic 'Alien' Sigourney Weaver played Ripley. What was Ripley's first name?

18. Dial Square was the original name of which Premier League football club?

19. In which year was children's TV favourite 'Newsround' first broadcast?
    a) 1972
    b) 1975
    c) 1978

20. A festival commemorating which saint is celebrated in Norway and Sweden each year on 13 December?
    a) St Lucy
    b) St Rachel
    c) St Monica

## Answers to Quiz 141: Films part 1

1. Silver Linings Playbook
2. Adam Sandler
3. George Clooney and Warren Beatty
4. Jennifer Lawrence
5. Jessica Chastain
6. Amour
7. Bane
8. Jeremy Renner
9. Emmanuelle Riva
10. Quvenzhané Wallis
11. Gone with the Wind
12. John Williams
13. None
14. Werner Herzog
15. Adrien Brody
16. Bob Hope
17. Beauty and the Beast
18. Phil Collins
19. Jeffrey
20. Kylie Minogue

DIFFICULT

# Quiz 143: History part 1

1. Martha Dandridge Custis was the wife of which US president?

2. The government of prime minister Mohammed Mosadegh was overthrown following a 1953 coup in which country?

3. In which decade was the World Trade Organization founded?

4. Which Irish prime minister signed the Good Friday Agreement?

5. In which modern-day country did the Battle of Pharsalus take place?

6. Which three kingdoms were united between 1397 and 1523 under the Kalmar Union?

7. Ivan the Terrible became Tsar of Russia in which century?

8. Spending just 228 days in charge, who had the shortest reign as British prime minister in the 20th century?

9. The so-called 'Yellow Revolution' of 1986 saw the overthrowing of the president of which Asian country?

10. Who resigned as West German Chancellor in 1974 after the discovery that one of his aides was an East German spy?

11. In which year did the Church of England ordain women priests for the first time?

12. What British newspaper was launched on 7 October 1986?

13. Erich Honecker was the long-time leader of which eastern-bloc country?

14. In which year was all-day opening in English and Welsh pubs allowed for the first time?

15. The terrorist known as 'Carlos the Jackal' was born in which country?

16. Who was the President of Israel between 1996 and 1999?

17. Who was executed in 2001 for carrying out the 1995 Oklahoma bombing?

18. Who was the first US president to address the Russian parliament?

19. How was Roman emperor Caesar Augustus related to Julius Caesar?
    a) cousin
    b) nephew
    c) great-nephew

20. In which decade of the 19th century was slavery abolished in Britain?
    a) 1820s
    b) 1830s
    c) 1840s

## Answers to Quiz 142: Pot Luck

1. Belgium
2. Kraftwerk
3. Moscow
4. Suriname
5. Denzel Washington
6. Absinthe
7. Adam Richman
8. The Second Punic War
9. Muttiah Muralitharan
10. Pablo Picasso
11. Gabon, Republic of Congo, Uganda, Kenya, and Somalia
12. Chicago
13. Clare Balding
14. Elderberry
15. Cairngorms
16. Juan Mata
17. Ellen
18. Arsenal
19. 1972
20. St Lucy

**DIFFICULT**

# Quiz 144: Pot Luck

1. Who was the first cricketer to score 500 runs in a single first-class innings?

2. Which British prime minister is said to have coined the phrase 'Every man has his price'?

3. Which country won football's 2013 Africa Cup of Nations?

4. Which team did they beat in the final?

5. In 2010, which country became first from South America to join the OECD?

6. Born in 1936, what is Lhamo Thondup more commonly known as?

7. 'A Doll's House', 'Hedda Gabler', and 'The Master Builder' are works by which Scandinavian playwright?

8. In which Italian city is the football club Sampdoria based?

9. Which 17th-century Dutch master said, 'Without atmosphere a painting is nothing'?

10. Britain's Jade Jones won a gold medal at the 2012 Olympic Games in which sport?

11. Punta Gallinas, the most northerly place in South America, is in which country?

12. Which castle, home to the Percy family since 1309, is known as 'the Windsor of the North'?

13. The Malacañang Palace is the official residence of the president of which Asian country?

14. Who played the president's son Robert in the 2012 film 'Lincoln'?

15. Australia is divided into how many different time zones?

16. What city, whose name is a familiar sight on the British High Street, is the capital of the Spanish region of Cantabria?

17. In which event did a four-year-old from Wallington called Jilly beat a three-year-old from Cesara, Italy, into second place in 2013?

18. A sculpture called 'The Pietà' was the only work signed by which artist?

19. Actor Alec Guinness, writer William S Burroughs, and boxer Joe Louis were all born in which year?
    a) 1910
    b) 1914
    c) 1918

20. Complete the title of the 2013 Disney animation: 'Wreck It ...'
    a) Ralph
    b) Rolf
    c) Ron

## Answers to Quiz 143: History part 1

1. George Washington
2. Iran
3. 1990s
4. Bertie Ahern
5. Greece
6. Norway, Sweden, and Denmark
7. 16th century
8. Andrew Bonar Law
9. The Philippines
10. Willy Brandt

11. 1994
12. The Independent
13. East Germany
14. 1988
15. Venezuela
16. Benjamin Netanyahu
17. Timothy McVeigh
18. Bill Clinton
19. Great-nephew
20. 1830s

**DIFFICULT**

# Quiz 145: Television part 1

1. Which band recorded the theme tune to the classic TV comedy 'Father Ted'?

2. Who was the subject of the 2012 TV biopic 'Filth'?

3. Which film director was the subject of the 2012 TV drama 'The Girl'?

4. In the 1960s TV series 'Batman', which villain was played by Frank Gorshin?

5. Dot.com billionaire Walden Schmidt is a character in which TV comedy?

6. What was the name of the First Officer of the Enterprise on 'Star Trek: The Next Generation'?

7. Which British actor played Dr Cal Lightman in the US crime drama 'Lie to Me'?

8. TV drama 'The Village' is set in which English county?

9. In cop drama 'New Tricks', what is the name of Brian's long-suffering wife?

10. Which 2003 political drama was turned into a 2009 Hollywood thriller starring Russell Crowe and Ben Affleck?

11. Which British actress made her debut as Olenna Tyrell in the third season of 'Game of Thrones'?

12. Which actor played Ronnie Barker's son in the Porridge spin-off 'Going Straight'?

13. What is the first name of the detective Foyle in the ITV drama 'Foyle's War'?

14. Who is the oldest of the six actors who played the main characters in 'Friends'?

15. Which British actress played Susan Wright in detective drama 'Broadchurch'?

Answers – page 297

16. In which year did 'Casualty' air for the first time?

17. Jack Malone, Sam Spade, and Viv Johnson were the central characters in which American police procedural?

18. Which stand-up comedian played Maxxie's dad Walter in the Channel 4 drama 'Skins'?

19. What is the occupation of TV experts Christian Jessen and Dawn Harper?
a) antique dealers
b) chefs
c) doctors

20. Who has made the most appearances as a guest on 'A Question of Sport'?
a) Steve Davis
b) Stephen Hendry
c) Michael Owen

## Answers to Quiz 144: Pot Luck

1. Brian Lara
2. Sir Robert Walpole
3. Nigeria
4. Burkina Faso
5. Chile
6. The Dalai Lama
7. Henrik Ibsen
8. Genoa
9. Rembrandt
10. Taekwondo
11. Colombia
12. Alnwick Castle
13. The Philippines
14. Joseph Gordon-Levitt
15. Three
16. Santander
17. The Best in Show at dog show Crufts
18. Michelangelo
19. 1914
20. Ralph

DIFFICULT

# Quiz 146: Pot Luck

1.  Which Shakespearean character utters the line, 'Cowards die many times before their deaths'?

2.  The Shin Bet is the domestic security service of which country?

3.  In which year was David Cameron elected as an MP for the first time?

4.  Who plays Steve McAndrew in the TV drama 'New Tricks'?

5.  US Congressman Jesse Jackson Jr admitted spending $22,500 in campaign funds to buy memorabilia about which musician?

6.  In February 2013, thieves stole diamonds worth $50m in a raid at which European airport?

7.  What nationality is the actor Gael Garcia Bernal?

8.  Which composer's fifth symphony was subtitled, 'A Soviet Artist's Response to Just Criticism'?

9.  A black-bean stew called 'feijoada' is a popular dish in which South American country?

10. Which American city is home to professional sports teams called the Nuggets and the Avalanche?

11. What is Australia's largest state by area?

12. Nord Kapp, the most northerly point in mainland Europe is in which country?

13. Daniel Day-Lewis played Daniel Plainview in which Oscar-nominated film?

14. Which artist refashioned his work 'For the Love of God' to raise funds for Comic Relief?

15. Ansaru is an Islamist movement based in which African country?

Answers – page 299

16. Which playwright won an Oscar for Best Original Screenplay for 'Shakespeare in Love'?

17. On which sport would you expect to hear commentators called Simon Holt, Graham Goode, and John Hunt?

18. Aqua fortis is an archaic term for which acid?

19. The coronet of which rank of the peerage features sixteen silver balls?
    a) Earl
    b) Duke
    c) Viscount

20. 'Work expands so as to fill the time available for its completion' is known as whose law?
    a) Norton's
    b) Parkinson's
    c) Ross's

## Answers to Quiz 145: Television part 1

1. The Divine Comedy
2. Mary Whitehouse
3. Alfred Hitchcock
4. The Riddler
5. Two and a Half Men
6. Will Riker
7. Tim Roth
8. Derbyshire
9. Esther
10. State of Play
11. Diana Rigg
12. Nicholas Lyndhurst
13. Christopher
14. Lisa Kudrow
15. Pauline Quirke
16. 1986
17. Without a Trace
18. Bill Bailey
19. Doctors
20. Steve Davis

DIFFICULT

# Quiz 147: Pop Music

1. Which British band's original name was Seymour?

2. Who was the first female artist to top the UK singles chart in five consecutive years?

3. Former professional footballer James Allan is the lead singer with which Scottish rock band?

4. Who is the only female performer to top the UK charts as a solo artist and as part of a duo, quartet, and quintet?

5. Which Whitney Houston chart-topper was the official anthem of the 1988 Olympic Games?

6. Who is the oldest member of Take That?

7. Which pop star was branded a 'moralizing slut' on Twitter by Russian politician Dmitry Rogozin in 2012?

8. 'Taller in More Ways' and 'Change' were chart-topping albums from which girl band?

9. Which band's 'Greatest Hits' is the biggest-selling UK album of all time?

10. Who was highest charting British male artist of 2012 with the single 'Impossible'?

11. What is the best-selling Comic Relief single?

12. 'Call Me Maybe' was a million-selling UK single in 2012 for which Canadian singer?

13. Which band were nominated for a Grammy for their work on the soundtrack to the 2010 film 'Tron Legacy'?

14. 'GRRR!' was a 2012 compilation album from which band?

15. Hip-hop star Wyclef Jean announced short-lived plans to stand for the president of which Caribbean country?

16. Girls Aloud were founded after winning which reality TV show?

17. Who was the youngest member of The Beatles?

18. Which European political leader released an album of love songs shortly after leaving office in 2011?

19. Which disco diva was inducted into the Rock and Roll Hall of Fame in 2013?
a) Gloria Gaynor
b) Donna Summer
c) Loleatta Holloway

20. Elizabeth Woolridge Grant is the real name of which American singer-songwriter?
a) Lady Gaga
b) Lana Del Rey
c) Rihanna

## Answers to Quiz 146: Pot Luck

1. Julius Caesar
2. Israel
3. 2001
4. Denis Lawson
5. Michael Jackson
6. Brussels
7. Mexican
8. Dmitri Shostakovich
9. Brazil
10. Denver
11. Western Australia
12. Norway
13. There Will Be Blood
14. Damien Hirst
15. Nigeria
16. Tom Stoppard
17. Horse racing
18. Nitric acid
19. Viscount
20. Parkinson's Law

DIFFICULT

# Quiz 148: Pot Luck

1. Which actor hosted the Oscars for the first time in 2013?

2. Which country joined the United Nations in July 2011?

3. 'Honi soit qui mal y pense' (Shame on him who thinks evil of it) is the motto of which order of chivalry?

4. The Sandor Palace is the official residence of the president of which European country?

5. Prior to running for the US presidency, Mitt Romney was the governor of which US state?

6. $HClO_3$ is the chemical formula for which acid?

7. Kakadu National Park is in which country?

8. In 2011, John Key started a second term as prime minister of which country?

9. Who resigned as leader of the Scottish Catholic Church in February 2013?

10. A little green monster named Om Nom is the main character in which app, which has been downloaded over 100 million times?

11. Which country is home to more lakes than the rest of the world combined?

12. What was the first Asian country to host the Winter Olympic Games?

13. Which poet and satirist coined the phrase, 'Fools rush in where angels fear to tread'?

14. Situated 515ft below sea level, Lake Assal is the lowest point of which continent?

15. Which animator, who died in 2013, was behind the cartoon favourites 'Roobarb and Custard' and 'Henry's Cat'?

16. Mega City One is a fictional city-state in the comic-book series featuring which law-enforcement officer?

17. What was the name of the 2012 feelgood French drama about a quadriplegic millionaire who hires a streetwise African to be his carer?

18. Which politician was at the centre of the so-called 'plebgate' affair?

19. The 2002 film 'City of God' was set in which country?
    a) Argentina
    b) Brazil
    c) Colombia

20. Angela Thorne, who played Marjory Frobisher in 'To the Manor Born' is the mother of which 'Spooks' star?

## Answers to Quiz 147: Pop Music

| | | | |
|---|---|---|---|
| 1. | Blur | 11. | Is This the Way to Amarillo? |
| 2. | Rihanna | 12. | Carly Rae Jepsen |
| 3. | Glasvegas | 13. | Daft Punk |
| 4. | Melanie C | 14. | The Rolling Stones |
| 5. | One Moment in Time | 15. | Haiti |
| 6. | Howard Donald | 16. | Popstars: The Rivals |
| 7. | Madonna | 17. | George Harrison |
| 8. | Sugababes | 18. | Silvio Berlusconi |
| 9. | Queen | 19. | Donna Summer |
| 10. | James Arthur | 20. | Lana Del Rey |

DIFFICULT

# Quiz 149: Animals

1. On the children's TV show 'Blue Peter', what type of animals were Maggie, Jim, Freda, and George?

2. How many hearts does an octopus have?

3. What type of creature is a cockchafer?

4. Hippocampus is another name for what type of marine creature?

5. Which animal's name derives from the Dutch for 'earth' and 'pig'?

6. 'Carassius auratus' is the Latin name for which common pet?

7. Which animal is sometimes described as the 'lion of the Andes'?

8. The yaffle, the great spotted, and the lesser spotted are species of which bird?

9. What class of animal derives its name from the Greek for 'living a double life'?

10. Shagreen is leather made from the skin of which animal?

11. What species of wild duck was also the title of a James Bond film?

12. What type of animals are classed as longwools, shortwools, and mountain breeds?

13. What type of creature is a flying fox?

14. Ophidiophobia is an abnormal fear of what type of animal?

15. What unit of weight is another name for the snow leopard?

16. 'Sturnus vulgaris' is the scientific name for which common bird?

17. The teal is a variety of what type of bird?

18. Egyptian, Griffon, Black, and Bearded are species of which bird?

19. What type of creature is a wrasse?
    a) bird
    b) fish
    c) insect

20. The constellation Lacerta takes its name from the Latin name for which animal?
    a) lizard
    b) rat
    c) snake

## Answers to Quiz 148: Pot Luck

1. Seth MacFarlane
2. South Sudan
3. The Most Noble Order of the Garter
4. Hungary
5. Massachusetts
6. Chloric acid
7. Australia
8. New Zealand
9. Cardinal Keith O'Brien
10. Cut the Rope
11. Canada
12. Japan
13. Alexander Pope
14. Africa
15. Bob Godfrey
16. Judge Dredd
17. Untouchable
18. Andrew Mitchell
19. Brazil
20. Rupert Penry-Jones

DIFFICULT

303

# Quiz 150: Pot Luck

1. 'The Birds' and 'The Clouds' are works by which ancient Greek poet and dramatist?

2. Who was younger when he became British prime minister – Tony Blair or David Cameron?

3. The film 'Man on Wire' tells the story of a tight-rope walker who walked between which pair of buildings?

4. In which year were the first Winter Olympic Games held?

5. Douglas Quaid is the central character in which 1990 sci-fi classic that was remade in 2012?

6. Steve Rodgers is the alter ego of which comic-book superhero?

7. Which American city is home to professional sports teams called the Flyers, 76ers, and Eagles?

8. Which actor provided the voice of the title character in the 2012 film comedy 'Ted'?

9. 'Friends applaud, the comedy is over' were the final words of which famous composer?

10. The equator passes through which three South American countries?

11. In 2013, it was announced that former Brookside star Mark Monaghan would be the narrator of which popular children's TV show?

12. Winnipeg is the capital and largest city of which Canadian province?

13. The ABCDE test is used to help identify what sort of cancer?

14. Sam Trickett, Antonio Esfandiari, and Daniel Negreanu are noted players of which game?

15. Which historian and broadcaster was elected as the MP for Stoke-on-Trent Central at the 2010 general election?

Answers – page 307

16. British home furnishings designer Cath Kidston is the cousin of which TV property expert?

17. How old was David Cameron when he became leader of the Conservative Party?

18. The prize awarded to the author of Britain's best theatre biography of the year is named after which critic?

19. In which field are Giles Deacon, Henry Holland, and Gareth Pugh notable names?
    a) fashion design
    b) classical music
    c) architecture

20. Composer Benjamin Britten, actor Peter Cushing, and US President Richard Nixon were all born in which year?
    a) 1912
    b) 1913
    c) 1914

## Answers to Quiz 149: Animals

| | |
|---|---|
| 1. Tortoises | 11. Goldeneye |
| 2. Three | 12. Sheep |
| 3. Beetle | 13. Bat |
| 4. Seahorse | 14. Snakes |
| 5. Aardvark | 15. Ounce |
| 6. Goldfish | 16. Starling |
| 7. Puma (cougar) | 17. Duck |
| 8. Woodpecker | 18. Vulture |
| 9. Amphibian | 19. Fish |
| 10. Shark | 20. Lizard |

DIFFICULT

# Quiz 151: Politics part 1

1. Prior to being elected mayor of London, Boris Johnson was the MP for which constituency?

2. In 2009, who became the first President of the European Council?

3. Who was Britain's first female Foreign Secretary?

4. Who was the first US president to address the UK Parliament?

5. Which ancient Greek philosopher said, 'Man by nature is a political animal'?

6. Who is the only candidate to receive over 65 million votes in a US presidential election?

7. Which well known chick-lit author was MP for Corby from 2010 until 2012?

8. In which year was the UK voting age reduced from 21 to 18?

9. By what name is the political blogger Paul Staines more commonly known?

10. Which best-selling author and journalist was the Labour candidate at the 2013 Eastleigh by-election?

11. Who resigned as Scotland's First Minister in 2001?

12. According to the US Constitution, an old presidency ends and a new one begins on which date?

13. The largest grouping in the European Parliament is the EPP. What do the initials EPP stand for?

14. Deacon was the Secret Service codename for which US President?

15. Which philosopher said, 'The price good men pay for indifference to public affairs is to be ruled by evil men'?

Answers – page 309

16. Which US president said, 'I would have made a good pope'?

17. In 2012, South African Nkosazana Dlamini-Zuma became the first woman to be elected leader of which organization?

18. The first US presidential inauguration took place in which city?

19. When was the last time a UK general election was not held on a Thursday?
    a) 1901
    b) 1931
    c) 1951

20. What was the turnout at the 2010 general election?
    a) 60.1%
    b) 65.1%
    c) 70.1%

## Answers to Quiz 150: Pot Luck

1. Aristophanes
2. David Cameron
3. The World Trade Center towers
4. 1924
5. Total Recall
6. Captain America
7. Philadelphia
8. Seth MacFarlane
9. Beethoven
10. Ecuador, Colombia, and Brazil
11. Thomas the Tank Engine
12. Manitoba
13. Skin cancer
14. Poker
15. Tristram Hunt
16. Kirstie Allsopp
17. 39
18. Sheridan Morley
19. Fashion design
20. 1913

DIFFICULT

# Quiz 152: Pot Luck

1.  In games of poker, what do the initials PLO stand for?

2.  Who became US president after the assassination of Abraham Lincoln?

3.  What actor connects the films 'Star Wars' and 'Carry On Henry'?

4.  Which country left the Commonwealth in 1949?

5.  MERCOSUR is a regional economic organization in which continent?

6.  What are the five London boroughs that begin with the letter B?

7.  Puyi was the last emperor of which country?

8.  The Catshuis is the official residence of the prime minister of which country?

9.  Which novelist, whose son is also an acclaimed author, won the Booker Prize for 'The Old Devils'?

10. Which comic-book superhero was also the nickname of former England football captain Bryan Robson?

11. 'Oinka Oinka Oinka why you awake' was the final tweet from which singer who died in 2011?

12. The radius is one of two long bones that make up the forearm. What is the other?

13. One of the main political groupings in the European Parliament is the ALDE. What do the initials ALDE stand for?

14. The ruined city of Chichen Itza is in which modern-day country?

15. Borborygmus is the technical name for what activity of the human body?

16. Which film that was nominated for the Best Picture Oscar in 2013 was based on a novel by Matthew Quick?

17. True or false – Pope Benedict XVI couldn't drive but he did hold a pilot's licence?

18. Allium sativum is the scientific name of which vegetable?

19. How many gold medals did the Great Britain team win at the 2012 Olympics?
    a) 28
    b) 29
    c) 30

20. Harry Melling, who played Harry Potter's cousin Dudley Dursley in the film franchise, is the grandson of which 'Dr Who'?
    a) Colin Baker
    b) John Pertwee
    c) Patrick Troughton

## Answers to Quiz 151: Politics part 1

1. Henley
2. Herman van Rompuy
3. Margaret Beckett
4. Ronald Reagan
5. Aristotle
6. Barack Obama
7. Louise Mensch (Bagshawe)
8. 1969
9. Guido Fawkes
10. John O'Farrell
11. Henry McLeish
12. 20 January
13. European People's Party
14. Jimmy Carter
15. Plato
16. Richard Nixon
17. The African Union
18. New York
19. 1951
20. 65.1%

DIFFICULT

# Quiz 153: Science and Technology

1. Whose law states that the absolute pressure and volume of a given mass of confined gas are inversely proportional?

2. What area of technology takes its name from from the Greek words for 'air' and 'to sail'?

3. A PET scan uses radiation to show the brain at work. What do the initials PET stand for?

4. In 1816, French physician René Laennec invented which medical instrument?

5. Which two elements are liquids at room temperature?

6. The USB is often used to transfer data from one computer to another. What do the initials USB stand for?

7. Oxygen is one of two elements of the periodic table that start with the letter O. What is the other?

8. Which British physicist shared the Nobel Prize in 1933 for his work on Heisenberg's theory of quantum mechanics?

9. Miranda is the smallest moon of which planet of the Solar System?

10. Which British scientist is best known for his 'Gaia hypothesis'?

11. What astronomical phenomenon are Quadrantids, Lyrids, and Eta Aquariids?

12. In computing, what does the acronym BIOS stand for?

13. Ben Silbermann is the founder of which pinboard-style photo-sharing website?

14. An angiogram is a special kind of x-ray that is used to examine what parts of the human body?

Answers – page 313

15. An internet domain ending with the letters .hr is from which country?

16. At what temperature are Celsius and Fahrenheit the same?

17. If all of the elements of the periodic table were listed alphabetically, which would be first on the list?

18. And which element would be last on the list?

19. Mark Pincus was the founder of which social-media company?
a) Tumblr  b) YouTube  c) Zynga

20. What nationality was the physicist and inventor of the centigrade thermometer, Anders Celsius?
a) Danish  b) Norwegian  c) Swedish

## Answers to Quiz 152: Pot Luck

1. Pot Limit Omaha
2. Andrew Johnson
3. David Prowse
4. Republic of Ireland
5. South America
6. Barking and Dagenham, Barnet, Bexley, Brent, and Bromley
7. China
8. The Netherlands
9. Sir Kingsley Amis
10. Captain Marvel
11. Amy Winehouse
12. Ulna
13. Alliance of Liberals and Democrats for Europe
14. Mexico
15. A rumbling stomach
16. Silver Linings Playbook
17. True
18. Garlic
19. 29
20. Patrick Troughton

DIFFICULT

# Quiz 154: Pot Luck

1. Which tennis star endorses a brand of sweets called Sugarpova?

2. Edwards Air Force Base is in which US state?

3. The headquarters of OPEC are in which country?

4. Who was the first non-European to be Secretary General of the United Nations?

5. Which country was he from?

6. Who, in June 2012, became the first woman to address the joint Houses of Parliament in Westminster Hall?

7. In the human body, by what name is the talus more commonly known?

8. The Coen Brothers' film 'True Grit' was based on a novel by which author?

9. Somavati Amavasya is a festival in which religion?

10. 'Solanum melongena' is the Latin name for which vegetable?

11. The Walker Art Gallery is located in which English city?

12. Which British actor provided the voice of King Harold in the film 'Shrek the Third'?

13. What is the European emergency telephone number?

14. Which fictional sleuth was killed off in the 1975 novel 'Curtain'?

15. The paintings 'Diana and Actaeon' and 'Diana and Callisto' are by which Renaissance master?

Answers – page 315

16. What nationality was Henri Nestle, the founder of the food and drinks company of the same name?

17. Who are the two Austrian drivers to have won the Formula One World Drivers' Championship?

18. The ciliary muscle can be found in which part of the human body?

19. Who topped the 'Most Influential Celebrities of 2013' list from Forbes magazine?
    a) Martin Scorsese
    b) Steven Spielberg
    c) Oprah Winfrey

20. In May 2013, a Chinese businessman paid a record-breaking €310,000 for a Belgian what?
    a) diamond
    b) dog
    c) racing pigeon

## Answers to Quiz 153: Science and Technology

| | |
|---|---|
| 1. Boyle's law (Robert Boyle) | 11. Meteor showers |
| 2. Aeronautics | 12. Basic Input/Output System |
| 3. Positron Emission Tomography | 13. Pinterest |
| 4. Stethoscope | 14. Arteries and veins |
| 5. Mercury and bromine | 15. Croatia |
| 6. Universal serial bus | 16. Minus 40 degrees |
| 7. Osmium | 17. Actinium |
| 8. Paul Dirac | 18. Zirconium |
| 9. Uranus | 19. Zynga |
| 10. James Lovelock | 20. Swedish |

DIFFICULT

# Quiz 155: Sport part 1

1. Alistair Brownlee won gold at London 2012 in which sport?

2. On which day of the year is a horse race called The King George VI Chase run?

3. Which striker won the Golden Boot award at the 2012 European Football Championships?

4. Which player from outside the British Isles won snooker's World Championship in 2010?

5. Who was the last player to win the men's singles at Wimbledon who was not from a country that began with the letter S (up to and including 2012)?

6. The football teams Young Boys and Grasshopper Club play in the top division in which European country?

7. Which rugby union team shares a ground with rugby league's Salford City Reds?

8. 'Between the Lines' was the autobiography of which British Olympic gold medallist?

9. The 2011 Wimbledon women's singles winner Petra Kvitova is from which country?

10. Which British golfer won 4 points out of 4 to help Europe to victory at the 2012 Ryder Cup?

11. Cricketers from which country were sent home from a 2013 tour to India for failing to provide a presentation on how the team could do better?

12. Which Welsh rugby player, who toured with the Lions in 1989, 1997, and 2001 was nicknamed 'Only the Good'?

13. Who is the youngest player to win a full international cap for the England football team?

14. The award-winning author Matthew Syed was formerly a British international in which sport?

15. David Rudisha was the only man to set an individual track athletics world record at the 2012 Olympics. In which event?

16. Who are the three 18-year-olds to have played for England at the finals of either the World Cup or the European Championships?

17. Roland Butcher was the first black player to represent England in which sport?

18. Who was the youngest man to captain the England football team?

19. Which team ended a 77-year drought when winning cricket's County Championship in 2011?
    a) Derbyshire  b) Lancashire  c) Northamptonshire

20. How many medals in total did the British team win at the 2012 Olympics?
    a) 60  b) 65  c) 70

## Answers to Quiz 154: Pot Luck

1.  Maria Sharapova
2.  California
3.  Austria
4.  U Thant
5.  Myanmar (Burma)
6.  Aung San Suu Kyi
7.  Ankle bone
8.  Charles Portis
9.  Hinduism
10. Aubergine
11. Liverpool
12. John Cleese
13. 112
14. Hercule Poirot
15. Titian
16. German
17. Niki Lauda and Jochen Rindt
18. The eye
19. Oprah Winfrey
20. Racing pigeon

DIFFICULT

# Quiz 156: Pot Luck

1. Which rank in the Royal Navy is equivalent to the British Army rank of Brigadier?

2. Bishopthorpe Palace is the official residence of which English clergyman?

3. Which dance fitness programme was created by Colombian Alberto 'Beto' Perez in the late 1990s?

4. Which Japanese city hosted the 1998 Winter Olympics?

5. Actress Jamie Lee Curtis is married to which star of cult comedy 'This Is Spinal Tap'?

6. TV smoothie Nigel Havers is the godfather of which comedian and actor who starred in the university drama 'Fresh Meat'?

7. Which media giant bought film production company Lucasfilm in 2012?

8. What is the name of the play by Peter Morgan about confidential meetings between the Queen and her twelve prime ministers?

9. Edward Kennedy were the real first names of which legendary jazz pianist?

10. 'I Hope I Get It', 'The Music and the Mirror', and 'The Tap Combination' are songs from which musical which enjoyed a West End revival in 2013?

11. In 2011, the Comedy Theatre in London was renamed in honour of which Nobel-winning playwright?

12. The World Trade Organization is based in which city?

13. In September 2011, Sir Bernard Hogan-Howe was appointed into what high-profile role?

Answers – page 319

14. The 1999 film 'Fight Club' is based on a novel by which author?

15. What was the best-selling video game of 2012?

16. Who was the first American First Lady to appear on the cover of the magazine 'Vogue'?

17. Former UN Secretary General Javier Perez de Cuellar is from which country?

18. In 2004, which British city became the first UNESCO City of Literature?

19. The first official UK chart for which genre of music was launched in 2013?
a) Christian music  b) country music  c) hip-hop

20. Membership of the Order of the Garter is limited to how many companions?
a) 22  b) 24  c) 26

## Answers to Quiz 155: Sport part 1

1. Triathlon
2. Boxing Day
3. Fernando Torres
4. Neil Robertson
5. Lleyton Hewitt
6. Switzerland
7. Sale Sharks
8. Victoria Pendleton
9. Czech Republic
10. Ian Poulter
11. Australia
12. Dai Young
13. Theo Walcott
14. Table tennis
15. Men's 800m
16. Michael Owen, Wayne Rooney, and Alex Oxlade-Chamberlain
17. Cricket
18. Bobby Moore
19. Lancashire
20. 65

DIFFICULT

# Quiz 157: Scotland

1. What is the second-longest river in Scotland?

2. The neolithic settlement of Skara Brae lies on which island group?

3. Which Scot was the first British cyclist to win the King of the Mountains competition at the Tour de France?

4. What is the official animal of Scotland?

5. The deepest freshwater loch on the British Isles is situated in the Scottish Highlands. What is it called?

6. The mountain Braeriach is in which range?

7. The McManus Galleries, Claypotts Castle, and the Mills Public Observatory are in which Scottish city?

8. William Wallace served as Guardian of Scotland until his defeat at which battle?

9. What name is given to mountains in Scotland that are over 3,000ft tall?

10. Completed in 2004, what high-profile building was designed by architect Enric Miralles?

11. The 1981 novel 'Lanark' and the 1992 Whitbread Prize winning book 'Poor Things' are works by which author?

12. 'The Blue Brazil' is the nickname of which Scottish football club?

13. Which award-winning Scottish film director's works include 'Ratcatcher', 'Morvern Callar', and 'We Need to Talk about Kevin'?

14. Aberdeenshire technology entrepreneur Pete Cashmore created which news and digital media company?

15. The world's oldest municipal fire service was founded in 1824 in which city?

16. The only remaining Battle of Britain airshow, which attracts crowds of 50,000 people, takes place at which RAF base located near St Andrews?

17. Which Scottish football club plays its home games at Gayfield Park?

18. St Kilda is the westernmost group of islands of which group?

19. England recognized the independence of Scotland following the signing of which treaty in 1328?
    a) Treaty of Derby
    b) Treaty of Northampton
    c) Treaty of Nottingham

20. Scotland is made up of approximately how many islands?
    a) 700
    b) 800
    c) 900

## Answers to Quiz 156: Pot Luck

1. Commodore
2. The Archbishop of York
3. Zumba
4. Nagano
5. Christopher Guest
6. Jack Whitehall
7. Disney
8. The Audience
9. Duke Ellington
10. A Chorus Line
11. Harold Pinter
12. Geneva
13. Commissioner of the Metropolitan Police
14. Chuck Palahniuk
15. Call of Duty: Black Ops II
16. Hillary Clinton
17. Peru
18. Edinburgh
19. Christian music
20. 24

DIFFICULT

# Quiz 158: Pot Luck

1. What are the seven London boroughs that start with the letter H?

2. Which of the Channel Islands was the last European territory to abolish feudal parliamentary representation?

3. George Bush International Airport serves which city?

4. 'Vicia faba' is the scientific name for which legume?

5. Which part of London was home to a greyhound track and is also the location of the William Morris Gallery?

6. What is the sixth largest country in the world by area?

7. The surname of which comedian is an anagram of 'Nairobi'?

8. Which Spice Girl played Mary Magdalene in the 2013 revival of 'Jesus Christ Superstar'?

9. What nationality is the award-winning film director Michael Haneke?

10. What do the initials CS in the name of novelist CS Lewis stand for?

11. Maxwell Montes is a mountain range on which planet of the Solar System?

12. The mythical creature the merlion is an emblem of which Asian country?

13. An artwork featuring a bus teetering on the roof of Bexhill's De La Warr Pavilion entitled 'Hang On a Minute Lads, I've Got a Great Idea' was based on a scene from which film?

14. What is the square root of 529?

15. 'Més que un club' is the motto of which European football club?

Answers – page 323

16. Which fruit appears on René Magritte's famous surrealist painting 'The Son of Man'?

17. Fallingwater House was the home of which influential American architect?

18. Which Renaissance painter was forced to flee Rome after killing a man over a dispute believed to involve a tennis match?

19. The navicula bone is found in which part of the human body?
    a) feet
    b) hands
    c) skull

20. In which year was the London Congestion Charge introduced?
    a) 2001
    b) 2002
    c) 2003

## Answers to Quiz 157: Scotland

1. River Spey
2. Orkney
3. Robert Millar
4. Unicorn
5. Loch Morar
6. The Cairngorms
7. Dundee
8. Battle of Falkirk
9. Munro
10. Scottish Parliament
11. Alasdair Gray
12. Cowdenbeath
13. Lynne Ramsay
14. Mashable
15. Edinburgh
16. RAF Leuchars
17. Arbroath
18. Outer Hebrides
19. Treaty of Northampton
20. 800

**DIFFICULT**

# Quiz 159: Colours

1. Hal Jordan is the alter ego of which comic-book superhero?

2. The medical condition methemoglobinemia can make the skin turn what colour?

3. Which British director's films include 'The Bourne Supremacy', 'The Bourne Ultimatum', and 'United 93'?

4. The painting 'Nude, Green Leaves, and Bust', which sold at auction for $106.5m, is by which artist?

5. Which Spice Girl founded the record label Red Girl Records?

6. Which pop star gave birth to a daughter called Blue Ivy in January 2012?

7. 'Grey Day' reached number 4 in the UK singles chart in 1981 for which band?

8. What is the surname of the title character in animated TV comedy 'The Cleveland Show'?

9. Which English county cricket team were for a time nicknamed the 'Brown Caps'?

10. 'The Truth About Love' was a 2012 album by which singer?

11. By what name is the puppet hero Paul Metcalfe better known?

12. What is the name of the actor who plays the foul-mouthed Irish matriarch in the TV comedy 'Mrs Brown's Boys'?

13. Which American band reached number 2 in the charts in 2012 with their album 'Overexposed'?

14. Medical drama 'Grey's Anatomy' is set in which US city?

15. What was the first novel written by Anne Brontë?

16. What District Line tube station lies between Fulham Broadway and Putney Bridge?

17. Which fashion retail magnate bought the Arcadia Group for £850m in 2002?

18. Italian football giants Juventus modelled their black and white striped kit on which English team?

19. Jacob Black is a character in which series of books?
    a) The Hunger Games
    b) Harry Potter
    c) Twilight

20. Alan White was the drummer with which of these bands?
    a) New Order
    b) Oasis
    c) The Smiths

## Answers to Quiz 158: Pot Luck

1. Hackney, Hammersmith and Fulham, Haringey, Harrow, Havering, Hillingdon, and Hounslow
2. Sark
3. Houston
4. Broad (fava) bean
5. Walthamstow
6. Australia
7. Dara O Briain
8. Melanie C
9. Austrian
10. Clive Staples
11. Venus
12. Singapore
13. The Italian Job
14. 23
15. Barcelona
16. Apple
17. Frank Lloyd Wright
18. Caravaggio
19. Feet
20. 2003

DIFFICULT

# Quiz 160: Pot Luck

1. Razz, badugi, and triple draw are variants of what type of game?

2. Which English scientist appeared on the £20 note from 1991 to 2001?

3. In finance, what do the initials BACS stand for?

4. The occipital bone is found in which part of the human body?

5. What vegetable is also known as the alligator pear?

6. Which British actor played the title character in the 2013 action film 'Parker'?

7. Which country covers a larger land area – Indonesia or Mexico?

8. Tharsis is an extensive volcanic area of which planet?

9. Britain's leading architecture prize is named after which architect?

10. The won is the currency of which two Asian countries?

11. Haldi is another name for what common spice?

12. Which actor portrayed Winston Churchill at the opening and closing ceremonies of the 2012 London Olympics?

13. Which band won the Mercury Prize in 2012 for their album 'An Awesome Wave'?

14. In the TV comedy 'Only Fools and Horses', what was Grandad Trotter's first name?

15. Who is the host of the science-based TV game show 'School of Hard Sums'?

Answers – page 327

16. What fruit is traditionally used in the Belgian beer 'kriek'?

17. What are the two racecourses in Norfolk?

18. Luguvalium was the Roman name for which northern English city?

19. The Royal Albert Memorial Museum and Art Gallery is in which English city?
    a) Bristol
    b) Exeter
    c) Plymouth

20. Who is the patron saint of silversmiths?
    a) St Cyprian
    b) St Dunstan
    c) St Monica

## Answers to Quiz 159: Colours

| | |
|---|---|
| 1. The Green Lantern | 11. Captain Scarlet |
| 2. Blue | 12. Brendan O'Carroll |
| 3. Paul Greengrass | 13. Maroon 5 |
| 4. Picasso | 14. Seattle |
| 5. Melanie C | 15. Agnes Grey |
| 6. Beyoncé | 16. Parsons Green |
| 7. Madness | 17. Sir Philip Green |
| 8. Brown | 18. Notts County |
| 9. Surrey | 19. Twilight |
| 10. Pink | 20. Oasis |

DIFFICULT

# Quiz 161: Places

1. Which tiny island state was formerly known as the Ellice Islands?

2. What was the first Asian country to host the Commonwealth Games?

3. The first Butlin's holiday camp opened in 1936 in which seaside resort?

4. Composer Gustav Holst was born in which English town?

5. 18th-century navigator Captain James Cook was murdered on which island group?

6. Van Diemen's Land is the former name of which island?

7. Which Asian capital is located on the Han River?

8. The Reeperbahn is a district of which European city?

9. The greyhound racing tracks at Perry Barr and Hall Green are in which English city?

10. The National Mining Museum of Wales is located in which town?

11. Sir Winston Churchill was born in which Oxfordshire stately home?

12. Shannon Airport lies in which Irish county?

13. The Lickey Hills are a group of hills 6km south-west of which English city?

14. The headquarters of the Open University are in which city?

15. In which English city is the National Space Science Centre located?

16. Which Belgian city is the world's biggest diamond centre?

17. Film director Ken Russell, comedian Benny Hill, and painter Sir John Everett Millais were all born in which English city?

18. The giant Burj Khalifa tower is in which city?

19. What was the first British city to introduce a congestion charge?
a) Durham
b) Leicester
c) Nottingham

20. In 2007, the visitor attraction Dickens World opened in which town?
a) Chatham
b) Margate
c) Portsmouth

## Answers to Quiz 160: Pot Luck

1. Poker
2. Michael Faraday
3. Bankers' Automated Clearing Services
4. Skull
5. Avocado
6. Jason Statham
7. Mexico
8. Mars
9. Sir James Stirling
10. North Korea and South Korea
11. Turmeric
12. Timothy Spall
13. Alt-J
14. Edward
15. Dara O Briain
16. Cherry
17. Fakenham and Yarmouth
18. Carlisle
19. Exeter
20. St Dunstan

DIFFICULT

# Quiz 162: Pot Luck

1. Loki is the archenemy of which comic-book superhero?

2. 'Petroselinum crispum' is another name for which popular herb?

3. A dry biscuit or cracker called the Oliver is associated with which English city?

4. A new gallery named after which artist opened in Margate in April 2011?

5. Which country covers a larger area – Germany or Japan?

6. Author CS Lewis and the late Labour politician Tony Banks were born in which city?

7. Prior to joining the euro, what was the currency of Malta?

8. ECOWAS is a trade organization in which continent?

9. What element of the periodic table is also the title of 2001 novel by Andrew Miller?

10. 'Graduation' was a 2007 chart-topping album by which American hip-hop star?

11. Which former editor of 'The Sun' wrote the acclaimed children's book 'The Truth About Leo'?

12. Which hugely popular board game, invented by Alfred Butts, celebrated its 60th birthday in 2008?

13. Which comedian and entertainer plays the trombone with the England football supporters' band?

14. What common drug is also known as acetylsalicylic acid?

15. In which year was the Bank of England £1 note withdrawn from circulation?

16. What was the biggest-selling DVD of the 2000s?

17. The 2005 novel 'Saturday' is by which acclaimed British writer?

18. Who plays Captain Jonathan Archer in sci-fi drama 'Star Trek: Enterprise'?

19. Which Scottish actor provided the voice of Gnomeo in the 2011 animated film 'Gnomeo and Juliet'?
    a) James McAvoy
    b) Ewan McGregor
    c) Sean Connery

20. In which branch of the arts is Gustavo Dudamel a notable name?
    a) classical music
    b) painting
    c) photography

## Answers to Quiz 161: Places

| | |
|---|---|
| 1. Tuvalu | 11. Blenheim Palace |
| 2. Malaysia | 12. Clare |
| 3. Skegness | 13. Birmingham |
| 4. Cheltenham | 14. Milton Keynes |
| 5. Hawaii | 15. Leicester |
| 6. Tasmania | 16. Antwerp |
| 7. Seoul | 17. Southampton |
| 8. Hamburg | 18. Dubai |
| 9. Birmingham | 19. Durham |
| 10. Blaenavon | 20. Chatham |

**DIFFICULT**

# Quiz 163: Wales

1. Which actor, best known for playing Q in the James Bond films, was born in Newport in 1914?

2. In which year did Wales qualify for football's World Cup for the first, and so far only, time?

3. The first act of union between Wales and England was signed in which century?

4. Which country controversially knocked Wales out of the 2011 Rugby World Cup at the semi-final stage?

5. Which member of the Monty Python team was born in Conwy?

6. The National Library of Wales is in which town?

7. What was published in Welsh for the first time in 1588?

8. What was the first town in Wales to be conferred city status?

9. In 1400, Owain Glyndŵr started a rebellion against which English king to establish an independent Wales?

10. In 1973, Brian Josephson became the first Welshman to be awarded what?

11. What type of food is known in Welsh as 'bara brith'?

12. How many MEPs does Wales elect to the European parliament?

13. What is the name of the actress who played Stacey in the TV sitcom 'Gavin and Stacey'?

14. Which Welsh castle is home to a tower that leans even further than the Leaning Tower of Pisa?

15. Up to the start of 2013, who were the four Welshmen to have managed a Premier League football club?

16. Which Welsh town hosted the 2012 World Alternative Games?

17. Who was the only Welshman to appear in England's 2005 Ashes-winning cricket team?

18. Gruff Rhys is the lead singer with which Welsh rock band?

19. In which year did the Welsh National Assembly open?
    a) 1999
    b) 2000
    c) 2001

20. Which Welsh singer finished second in the 2012 series of the US version of 'Strictly Come Dancing'?
    a) Shirley Bassey
    b) Katherine Jenkins
    c) Tom Jones

## Answers to Quiz 162: Pot Luck

1. Thor
2. Parsley
3. Bath
4. Turner
5. Japan
6. Belfast
7. Maltese lira
8. Africa
9. Oxygen
10. Kanye West
11. David Yelland
12. Scrabble
13. Bernie Clifton
14. Aspirin
15. 1988
16. Mamma Mia!
17. Ian McEwan
18. Scott Bakula
19. James McAvoy
20. Classical music

**DIFFICULT**

# Quiz 164: Pot Luck

1. Which character carried the Olympic flame in an episode of 'EastEnders' aired in the run up to the 2012 games?

2. Paul Heaton, Norman Cook, Stan Cullimore, and Dave Hemingway were members of which 1980s pop group?

3. By what name is the comic-book character Selina Kyle more commonly known?

4. Which Italian dessert translates into English as 'pick me up'?

5. What alliterative two word phrase is used to describe a style of football, favoured by Spanish teams, that involves short passing and movement?

6. Who was the pope during the Second World War?

7. Who is the Roman equivalent of Demeter, the Greek goddess of the earth and agriculture?

8. Which of the Seven Wonders of the World was built by the widowed Queen Artemisia in around 350 BC?

9. In which country is the Taklimakan Shamo desert?

10. 'Two Weeks One Summer' was a 2012 exhibition of paintings by which contemporary British artist?

11. Which orchestra is resident at London's Barbican Centre?

12. With basements extending 24.5m underground, which London building was the largest building constructed in the UK in the 20th century?

13. Which fruit is used to flavour the Italian liqueur maraschino?

14. Which American novelist, who was born in 1789 and died in 1851, wrote the series of historical novels known as the 'Leatherstocking Tales'?

15. 'Through Thick and Thin' was the title of the 2011 autobiography from which TV fashion guru?

Answers – page 335

16. The giant Pinkpop Festival is a musical event in which European country?

17. In 1694 Sir John Houblon became the first governor of which organization?

18. The name of which Israeli political party translates into English as 'consolidation'?

19. Who was the only European to appear on Forbes magazine's list of most influential celebrities in 2013?
a) Victoria Beckham
b) Bono
c) Hugh Grant

20. Which of the following countries covers the largest area?
a) Finland
b) Norway
c) Sweden

## Answers to Quiz 163: Wales

1. Desmond Llewelyn
2. 1958
3. 16th
4. France
5. Terry Jones
6. Aberystwyth
7. The Bible
8. Bangor
9. King Henry IV
10. A Nobel Prize
11. Speckled bread
12. Four
13. Joanna Page
14. Caerphilly Castle
15. Chris Coleman, Mark Hughes, Tony Pulis, and Mike Walker
16. Llanwrtyd Wells
17. Simon Jones
18. Super Furry Animals
19. 1999
20. Katherine Jenkins

**DIFFICULT**

# Quiz 165: Sporting Nicknames

Identify the sports stars from the following nicknames:

1.  Silverback (darts)

2.  The Divine Ponytail (football)

3.  The Cannibal (cycling)

4.  The Rat (motor racing)

5.  The Beast (athletics)

6.  The Raging Potato (rugby union)

7.  The King of Spain (cricket)

8.  Pacman (boxing)

9.  The Count (darts)

10. One Size (football)

11. The Sheriff of Pottingham (snooker)

12. The Executioner (boxing)

13. The Rawalpindi Express (cricket)

14. The Cobra (boxing)

15. Chariots (rugby league)

Answers – page 337

16.  The Baby-Faced Assassin (football)

17.  The Sherminator (cricket)

18.  The Machine (darts)

19.  The Pirate (cycling)

20.  The Turbanator (cricket)

## Answers to Quiz 164: Pot Luck

1.  Billy Mitchell
2.  The Housemartins
3.  Catwoman
4.  Tiramasu
5.  Tiki taka
6.  Pius XII
7.  Ceres
8.  The Mausoleum of Halicarnassus
9.  China
10. Damien Hirst
11. London Symphony Orchestra
12. British Library
13. Cherry
14. James Fenimore Cooper
15. Gok Wan
16. The Netherlands
17. The Bank of England
18. Likud
19. Bono
20. Sweden

**DIFFICULT**

# Quiz 166: Pot Luck

1. Which director, whose films included 'Top Gun', 'Days of Thunder', and 'True Romance', died after jumping from a Los Angeles bridge in August 2012?

2. Liverpool boss Brendan Rodgers started his career in football management with which club?

3. What was the name of the short-lived BBC soap opera set on Spain's Costa del Sol?

4. Who was the first woman to win the Booker Prize twice?

5. Which footballer turned TV pundit's 2012 autobiography was called 'Red'?

6. Which country covers a larger area – the UK or Romania?

7. 'Manly deeds, womanly words' is the motto of which American state?

8. Which American author wrote the short story 'The Million Pound Bank Note' which was later turned into a film starring Gregory Peck?

9. Which long-running TV quiz show celebrated its 50th birthday in September 2012?

10. In which year did the UK's first curry house open?

11. Who in 2013 became only the fourth English cricketer to take 300 Test wickets?

12. Prior to becoming pope in 2013, Jorge Mario Bergoglio was the archbishop of which diocese?

13. Who comes next on this list and why: Linda Eastman, Heather Mills, _____?

14. Who resigned as Director General of the BBC in November 2012 after just 54 days in the post?

15. What was the name of the doctor convicted of the involuntary manslaughter of Michael Jackson?

16. Named after a Canadian prime minister, a wolf dog called Diefenbaker was a central character in which 1990s American police drama?

17. Belmopan is the capital city of which Commonwealth country?

18. Henry Sewell was the first prime minster of which Commonwealth country?

19. In 2012, Gawain Jones was crowned British champion in which game?
    a) backgammon  b) chess  c) poker

20. Aussie actress and singer Holly Vallance is a relative of which British comedian?
    a) Benny Hill  b) Frankie Howerd  c) Peter Sellers

## Answers to Quiz 165: Sporting Nicknames

1. Tony O'Shea
2. Roberto Baggio
3. Eddy Merckx
4. Niki Lauda
5. Yohan Blake
6. Keith Wood
7. Ashley Giles
8. Manny Pacquiao
9. Ted Hankey
10. Fitz Hall
11. Anthony Hamilton
12. Bernard Hopkins
13. Shoaib Akhtar
14. Carl Froch
15. Martin Offiah
16. Ole Gunnar Solskjaer
17. Ian Bell
18. James Wade
19. Marco Pantani
20. Harbhajan Singh

DIFFICULT

# Quiz 167: Name the Year

1. In which year did Ken Livingstone become the first directly elected Mayor of London?

2. Sir Isaac Newton was born in the same year that Galileo died. Which year?

3. In which year did Queen Elizabeth the Queen Mother and Princess Margaret die?

4. TV show 'The Apprentice' first aired in which year?

5. In which year was Nelson Mandela released from prison?

6. The first football World Cup hosted in Europe took place in which year?

7. The first direct elections to the European Parliament were held in which year?

8. The Beatles had their first UK number one single in which year?

9. In which year was the first Cricket World Cup held?

10. In which year did the Spanish Civil War start?

11. In which year did India gain independence from Britain?

12. The world's first test-tube baby was born in which year?

13. In which year did the Switzerland host football's World Cup?

14. Nigel Mansell won his only Formula One World Drivers' Championship title in which year?

15. John Paul II succeeded John Paul I as Pope in which year?

16. The official UK singles chart was launched in which year?

17. In which year did Winston Churchill die?

18. The Battle of Gettysburg was fought in which year?

19. In which year was the film 'Star Wars' released?

20. Roger Federer won his first Wimbledon title in which year?

## Answers to Quiz 166: Pot Luck

1. Tony Scott
2. Watford
3. Eldorado
4. Hilary Mantel
5. Gary Neville
6. UK
7. Maryland
8. Mark Twain
9. University Challenge
10. 1810
11. James Anderson
12. Buenos Aires
13. Nancy Shevell (wives of Paul McCartney)
14. George Entwistle
15. Dr Conrad Murray
16. Due South
17. Belize
18. New Zealand
19. Chess
20. Benny Hill

**DIFFICULT**

# Quiz 168: Pot Luck

1. Implemented by the US government in response to the 2008 financial crisis, what do the initials TARP stand for?

2. 'Omnia omnibus ubique' is the motto of which shop?

3. In 2009, George Abela became the president of which European country?

4. Which singer played Marius in the original West End production of 'Les Miserables'?

5. In which city is the football team Galatasaray based?

6. Which 19th-century English poet, who was married to another poet, wrote the poems 'The Cry of the Children', Sonnets from the Portuguese' and 'Aurora Leigh'?

7. Olympic wrestler turned actor Harold Sakata is best known for playing which James Bond baddie?

8. Ian Anderson is the flautist and front-man of which veteran rock band?

9. Screenwriter and film producer Jane Goldman is married to which British broadcaster?

10. The 'Intercrime' series of novels are by which award-winning Swedish author?

11. Pussycat Doll Ashley Roberts finished second in which 2012 reality TV show?

12. Ralf Hütter and Florian Schneider were the original members of which band?

13. Take That star Robbie Williams is a fan of which football club?

14. The Lakeside Hammers and Swindon Robins are teams that compete in which sport?

15. Funafuti is the capital city of which Commonwealth country?

16. Which TV serial killer is based on the novels of Jeff Lindsay?

17. Which 66/1 outsider won the 2013 Grand National?

18. In 1874, whom did Benjamin Disraeli succeed as British prime minister?

19. Which American state has the longest border with Mexico?
    a) Arizona
    b) California
    c) Texas

20. Which classic Alfred Hitchcock film was based on a short story by Daphne du Maurier?
    a) 'The Birds'
    b) 'Psycho'
    c) 'Rear Window'

## Answers to Quiz 167: Name the Year

| | | | |
|---|---|---|---|
| 1. | 2000 | 11. | 1947 |
| 2. | 1642 | 12. | 1978 |
| 3. | 2002 | 13. | 1954 |
| 4. | 2005 | 14. | 1992 |
| 5. | 1990 | 15. | 1978 |
| 6. | 1934 | 16. | 1952 |
| 7. | 1979 | 17. | 1965 |
| 8. | 1963 | 18. | 1863 |
| 9. | 1975 | 19. | 1977 |
| 10. | 1936 | 20. | 2003 |

DIFFICULT

# Quiz 169: Films part 2

1. Starring Donald Sutherland and Julie Christie, the classic 1973 film 'Don't Look Now' was based on a short story by which author?

2. Kate Winslet won the Best Actress Oscar in 2008 for her performance in which film?

3. What was the first name of the James Bond villain 'Goldfinger'?

4. Who played the US president Benjamin Asher in the 2013 thriller 'Olympus Has Fallen'?

5. What was the first horror film to be nominated for a Best Picture Oscar?

6. Kevin Costner played Lieutenant John Dunbar in which Oscar-winning film?

7. What is 'Rick's' surname in the wartime classic 'Casablanca'?

8. Who played Legolas Greenleaf in 'The Lord of the Rings'?

9. Measuring some 6ft 5in, who in 2004 became the tallest recipient of an Oscar for his performance in 'Mystic River'?

10. Nicholas Angel and Danny Butterman are the names of the policemen in which 2007 British comedy adventure starring Simon Pegg?

11. Which actor played The Riddler in the 1995 film 'Batman Forever'?

12. Who directed the award-winning 2006 war drama 'Flags of Our Fathers'?

13. What was the second film in the long-running 'Carry On ...' series of comedies?

14. Which American movie critic, who died in 2013, was the first person to receive a Pulitzer Prize for film criticism?

15. Which actress played Natasha Romanoff and her alter ego the Black Widow in the 2012 film 'The Avengers'?

16. What was the name of the character played by Ursula Andress in the James Bond film 'Dr No'?

17. Which former Dr Who played Radagast the Brown in the 2012 film 'The Hobbit'?

18. Which Scottish actor played Dr Alfred 'Fred' Jones in the 2011 drama 'Salmon Fishing in the Yemen'?

19. Complete the title of the 2013 British thriller: 'Welcome to the ...'
    a) End  b) Pleasuredome  c) Punch

20. Which Blue Peter presenter appeared in the film musical 'Bugsy Malone'?
    a) Mark Curry  b) Peter Duncan  c) Sarah Greene

## Answers to Quiz 168: Pot Luck

1. Troubled Asset Relief Program
2. Harrods
3. Malta
4. Michael Ball
5. Istanbul
6. Elizabeth Barrett Browning
7. Oddjob
8. Jethro Tull
9. Jonathan Ross
10. Arne Dahl
11. I'm a Celebrity ... Get Me out of Here!
12. Kraftwerk
13. Port Vale
14. Speedway
15. Tuvalu
16. Dexter
17. Auroras Encore
18. Gladstone
19. Texas
20. The Birds

DIFFICULT

# Quiz 170: Pot Luck

1.  Herpes zoster is another name for which viral infection?

2.  In Greek mythology, who was the wife of Odysseus and the mother of Telemachus?

3.  'The Sound of Laughter' was the title of the 2006 autobiography from which popular British comedian?

4.  'Moonraker' is a nickname given to people from which English county?

5.  Which author wrote the feminist classic 'The Second Sex'?

6.  Which German engineer invented the internal-combustion engine that bears his name?

7.  Charles Lutwidge Dodgson was the real name of which 19th-century English author?

8.  Who was the first Scot to be appointed Poet Laureate?

9.  'Stabat Mater' and 'From the New World' are works by which Czech composer?

10. What was the first name of the poet Lord Byron?

11. Which comedian edited 'The Beano' as part of the 2013 Comic Relief fund-raising festivities?

12. The most westerly point of the United Kingdom is in which Northern Irish county?

13. Nell Trent is the central character in which novel by Charles Dickens?

14. Bright's disease affects which organ of the human body?

15. Which famous music event was billed as 'An Aquarian Exposition: 3 Days of Peace & Music'?

16. In 2013, who became the first crime writer to be made a member of the Forensic Science Society?

17. Which Dutch navigator and explorer discovered New Zealand, Tonga, and the Fiji Islands?

18. Which French philosopher, who was born in 1798, was the founder of positivism?

19. In 2013 it was revealed that Prince Charles had been attempting to learn which language?
    a) Arabic
    b) Mandarin
    c) Welsh

20. 'Fidelis ad mortem' (Faithful unto death) is the motto of the Police Department of which American city?
    a) Chicago
    b) Los Angeles
    c) New York

## Answers to Quiz 169: Films part 2

| | | | |
|---|---|---|---|
| 1. | Daphne du Maurier | 11. | Jim Carrey |
| 2. | The Reader | 12. | Clint Eastwood |
| 3. | Auric | 13. | Carry on Nurse |
| 4. | Aaron Eckhart | 14. | Roger Ebert |
| 5. | The Exorcist | 15. | Scarlett Johansson |
| 6. | Dances With Wolves | 16. | Honey Ryder |
| 7. | Blaine | 17. | Sylvester McCoy |
| 8. | Orlando Bloom | 18. | Ewan McGregor |
| 9. | Tim Robbins | 19. | Punch |
| 10. | Hot Fuzz | 20. | Mark Curry |

DIFFICULT

# Quiz 171: Television part 2

1. What is the first name of the title character played by Sean Bean in the Napoleonic-era drama 'Sharpe'?

2. Which alliterative presenter hosts the TV panel show 'Big Ask'?

3. Which bird was also the title of a 2012 BBC comedy starring Greg Davies and Helen Baxendale?

4. Shostakovich's Prelude No. 15 was the theme tune to which popular 1980s sitcom?

5. Which adventure drama was described by one of its creators as 'The Sopranos in Middle Earth'?

6. Which British actor played the title character in the 1980s drama 'The Charmer'?

7. 'For Anyone' by the band Beady Eye was the theme tune to which short-lived sitcom starring Will Mellor and Warren Clarke?

8. In the TV comedy 'Open All Hours', what was tight-fisted shopkeeper Arkwright's first name?

9. Who was the youngest presenter of children's TV show 'Blue Peter'?

10. Who are the two rugby players to have won 'Celebrity Masterchef'?

11. Who plays the title character in the BBC comedy 'Being Eileen'?

12. The million-selling single 'Eye Level' by the Simon Park Orchestra was the theme to which detective drama?

13. Ian Fletcher, Kay Hope, and Sally Owen were central characters in which TV comedy?

14. Which British actor, best known for playing Chief Inspector Wexford, was born in Bulgaria?

15. What is the name of the actor who plays the title character in 'Foyle's War'?

16. Which actor, who died in 2012, played loveable slob Onslow in 'Keeping Up Appearances' and Twiggy in 'The Royle Family'?

17. Leanne Mitchell was the first winner of which TV talent show?

18. Who played Detective Sergeant Hathaway in the detective drama 'Lewis'?

19. The political drama 'Borgen' is set in which country?
    a) Denmark
    b) Norway
    c) Sweden

20. Which comedian stars in children's TV show 'The Ministry of Curious Stuff"?
    a) Jack Dee
    b) Ben Miller
    c) Vic Reeves

## Answers to Quiz 170: Pot Luck

1. Shingles
2. Penelope
3. Peter Kay
4. Wiltshire
5. Simone de Beauvoir
6. Rudolf Diesel
7. Lewis Carroll
8. Carol Ann Duffy
9. Antonín Dvořák
10. George
11. Harry Hill
12. Fermanagh
13. The Old Curiosity Shop
14. Kidney
15. The Woodstock festival
16. Lynda La Plante
17. Abel Tasman
18. Auguste Comte
19. Arabic
20. New York

DIFFICULT

# Quiz 172: Pot Luck

1.  Royston Vasey is the real name of which British stand-up comedian?

2.  Which actor played the psychopathic Begbie in the 1996 film 'Trainspotting'?

3.  True or false – the wife of UKIP leader Nigel Farage is German?

4.  The 'Museu Calouste Gulbenkian' is in which European capital city?

5.  Who was the US vice-president during Jimmy Carter's presidency?

6.  In 2009, toy maker Mattel created a Barbie doll based on which politician?

7.  'Parce que je le vaux bien' is the French for which advertising catchphrase?

8.  Which Hindu goddess of wealth and good fortune was the wife of Vishnu?

9.  King Robert Baratheon and Lord Eddard 'Ned' Stark are characters in which TV drama?

10.  'Jackpot' is the nickname of which darting world champion?

11.  In November 2012 comedian David Mitchell married which journalist, broadcaster, and poker player?

12.  Which tour operator's first organized excursion was an 1841 trip from Leicester to Loughborough?

13.  What make of car was named after the daughter of Austrian banker and car-lover Emile Jellinek?

14.  Who was the mother of King Edward VI?

15.  King Farouk I, who abdicated after a 1952 coup, was the last king of which country?

Answers – page 351

16. Which country shares borders with Armenia, Azerbaijan, Russia, and Turkey?

17. 'The Social Contract' is a work by which 18th-century Swiss-born, French political philosopher?

18. The Vltava River flows through which European capital?

19. McDiarmid Park is the home ground of which Scottish football club?
    a) Falkirk
    b) St Johnstone
    c) St Mirren

20. Steve Marriott was the lead singer with which 1960s band?
    a) The Kinks
    b) The Small Faces
    c) The Who

## Answers to Quiz 171: Television part 2

1. Richard
2. Alexander Armstrong
3. Cuckoo
4. Ever Decreasing Circles
5. Game of Thrones
6. Nigel Havers
7. In with the Flynns
8. Albert
9. Yvette Fielding
10. Matt Dawson and Phil Vickery
11. Sue Johnston
12. Van der Valk
13. Twenty Twelve
14. George Baker
15. Michael Kitchen
16. Geoffrey Hughes
17. The Voice
18. Laurence Fox
19. Denmark
20. Vic Reeves

DIFFICULT

# Quiz 173: Europe

1. Akureyri is the second largest city in which European country?

2. 'La Sapienza' is a university based in which European city?

3. Ratoncito Pérez is the Spanish equivalent of which mythical benefactor?

4. The giant Gothic cathedral in which German city took 632 years to build?

5. Portela Airport serves which European city?

6. The giant Strahov Stadium is in which European capital?

7. The Gulf of Bothnia lies between which two countries?

8. Cape Saint Vincent is the most south-westerly point of which European country?

9. Burgas, Ruse, and Sliven are cities in which country?

10. Linate Airport serves which major European city?

11. Franz Josef Land is a 191-island archipelago belonging to which country?

12. What is the name of the Russian exclave that lies between Poland and Lithuania on the Baltic Sea?

13. The Tagus River flows through which two countries?

14. Originally commissioned in 1357 and reconstructed in 1970, the Charles Bridge is in which city?

15. Nový čas is a best-selling tabloid newspaper in which country?

16. What is the currency of Liechtenstein?

17. Heraklion is the capital city of which Greek island?

18. The Thyssen-Bornemisza Museum is in which European capital?

19. The Seimas is the parliament of which EU member country?
    a) Latvia
    b) Estonia
    c) Lithuania

20. Treptower Park is an attraction in which European capital city?
    a) Berlin
    b) Brussels
    c) Paris

## Answers to Quiz 172: Pot Luck

1.  Roy 'Chubby' Brown
2.  Robert Carlyle
3.  True
4.  Lisbon
5.  Walter Mondale
6.  Angela Merkel
7.  Because I'm Worth It
8.  Lakshmi (sometimes called Shri)
9.  Game of Thrones
10. Adrian Lewis
11. Victoria Coren
12. Thomas Cook
13. Mercedes
14. Jane Seymour
15. Egypt
16. Georgia
17. Jean-Jacques Rousseau
18. Prague
19. St Johnstone
20. The Small Faces

DIFFICULT

# Quiz 174: Pot Luck

1. Which six countries have borders with the Black Sea?

2. Durrës is the second largest city of which European country?

3. In Greek mythology, which king fell in love with a statue?

4. 'Sweet Tooth' is a 2013 novel by which award-winning British novelist?

5. St George was adopted as patron saint of England by which monarch?

6. In 2007, a bronze statue created by sculptor Anthony Dufort of which politician was unveiled in the Parliament Members' Lobby?

7. Which actor-turned-director made the films 'Willow', 'The Da Vinci Code', and 'Frost: Nixon'?

8. In 2011, Pedro Passos Coelho was elected president of which country?

9. Actor Brad Pitt, politician John Bercow, and guitarist Johnny Marr were all born in which year?

10. Who created the fictional Venetian detective Guido Brunetti?

11. 'Life Thru a Lens' was the first number one solo album from which recording artist?

12. French President François Hollande was given which animal as a gift of thanks from the people of Mali following France's involvement in ridding that country of Islamist rebels?

13. Classical musician Janina Fialkowska is a world-renowned performer on which instrument?

14. Which Liverpool-born actor played Professor Quirinus Quirrell in 'Harry Potter and the Philosopher's Stone'?

Answers – page 355

15. Which soft drink was created by Charles Leiper Grigg of the Howdy Corporation in 1920?

16. Sharon Stone received her only Oscar nomination for which film?

17. 'So Me' was the 2004 autobiography of which Irish broadcaster?

18. The influential bands Tangerine Dream and Can are from which country?

19. Which British author created the TV detective drama 'Foyle's War'?
    a) Sebastian Faulks
    b) Anthony Horowitz
    c) Louis de Bernieres

20. Patrick Cox is a noted maker of what?
    a) hats
    b) dresses
    c) shoes

## Answers to Quiz 173: Europe

1. Iceland
2. Rome
3. The tooth fairy
4. Cologne
5. Lisbon
6. Prague
7. Sweden and Finland
8. Portugal
9. Bulgaria
10. Milan
11. Russia
12. Kaliningrad Oblast
13. Spain and Portugal
14. Prague
15. Slovakia
16. The Swiss Franc
17. Crete
18. Madrid
19. Lithuania
20. Berlin

**DIFFICULT**

# Quiz 175: Alliterative Answers part 1

1. Which former runner-up on 'The X Factor' represented the United Kingdom at the 2008 Eurovision Song Contest?

2. What 2001 film starred Jake Gyllenhaal as a troubled teenager who had visions of a giant rabbit called Frank?

3. Stephen Graham played which footballer in the 2009 film 'The Damned United'?

4. Which American thriller writer created the characters Dirk Pitt and Isaac Bell?

5. The theme song to the film 'Ghostbusters II' was sung by which R&B singer?

6. Who was the Children's Laureate from 2003 until 2005?

7. Who sang 'You Know My Name', the theme to the 2006 Bond film 'Casino Royale'?

8. Which Archbishop presided over the royal wedding of Prince Charles and Lady Diana Spencer?

9. Which actress plays the lead character in the US drama 'The Big C'?

10. Which comedian plays Lee's dad Frank in the BBC sitcom 'Not Going Out'?

11. Who is the leading wicket-taker in the history of Test cricket?

12. Who in 1999 became the first First Minister of Scotland?

13. Which cricket umpire is known for his crooked finger?

14. Who was the only Englishman to win the European Footballer of the Year award more than once?

15. What is the real name of rapper Eminem?

16. Who played Professor Sprout in the 'Harry Potter' films?

17. Which British author wrote the 1959 novel 'Cider with Rosie'?

18. Which 2000 romantic comedy starred Mel Gibson as a chauvinistic executive who unexpectedly gained the ability to hear what women are really thinking?

19. 'Peeling The Onion' is the title of the autobiography of which German writer who won the Nobel Prize for Literature in 1999?

20. What was the name of the character played by Ray Liotta in the gangster classic 'Goodfellas'?

## Answers to Quiz 174: Pot Luck

1. Ukraine, Russia, Georgia, Turkey, Bulgaria, and Romania
2. Albania
3. Pygmalion
4. Ian McEwan
5. Edward III
6. Margaret Thatcher
7. Ron Howard
8. Portugal
9. 1963
10. Donna Leon
11. Robbie Williams
12. Camel
13. Piano
14. Ian Hart
15. 7 Up
16. Casino
17. Graham Norton
18. Germany
19. Anthony Horowitz
20. Shoes

DIFFICULT

# Quiz 176: Pot Luck

1. In Greek mythology, which king was forced to push a giant stone up a hill only to see it roll down once it reached the top?

2. The Falasha are members of the Jewish faith from which country?

3. The phrase 'for whom the bell tolls' comes from a work by which metaphysical poet?

4. The words admiral, almanac, and mattress derive from which language?

5. Who played Sonny Corleone in the crime classic 'The Godfather'?

6. 'Murder Most Fab', 'Devil In Disguise', and 'Briefs Encountered' are novels by which British comedian?

7. Lyallpur is the former name of which Pakistani city?

8. Matt Bellamy is the lead vocalist with which successful British rock band?

9. Who succeeded Nelson Mandela as President of South Africa?

10. Which architect designed Marble Arch and the Brighton Pavilion?

11. 'A Pure Woman Faithfully Presented' is the subtitle of which 1891 novel?

12. Prior to becoming the Roman Catholic Archbishop of Westminster, Vincent Nichols was the Archbishop of which diocese?

13. 'The Original of Laura', the unfinished novel of which Russian-born writer who died in 1977, was finally published in 2009?

14. Which 19th-century English priest was beatified in 2010?

15. Which playwright in 1992 became the first president of the newly created Czech Republic?

16. 'Swept Away', 'Revolver', and 'RocknRolla' are films from which British director?

17. 'The Nova Trilogy' is a collection of experimental novels by which American author?

18. Who was the only fashion designer to appear on 'Time' magazine's list of 100 most influential people of the 20th century?

19. The Stephen Joseph Theatre is in which English seaside town?
    a) Scarborough  b) Southend-on-Sea  c) Southport

20. Which actress and comedian was on the judging panel of TV talent show 'Superstar'?
    a) Jo Brand  b) Dawn French  c) Jennifer Saunders

## Answers to Quiz 175: Alliterative Answers part 1

1.  Andy Abraham
2.  Donnie Darko
3.  Billy Bremner
4.  Clive Cussler
5.  Bobby Brown
6.  Michael Morpurgo
7.  Chris Cornell
8.  Robert Runcie
9.  Laura Linney
10. Bobby Ball
11. Muttiah Muralitharan
12. Donald Dewar
13. Billy Bowden
14. Kevin Keegan
15. Marshall Mathers
16. Miriam Margolyes
17. Laurie Lee
18. What Women Want
19. Gunter Grass
20. Henry Hill

DIFFICULT

# Quiz 177: Alliterative Answers part 2

1. Who was the first footballer to win 100 caps for the Republic of Ireland?

2. Whom did David Cameron beat in the election to become leader of the Conservative Party?

3. Which actor played the sadistic Mr Blonde in the 1992 crime drama 'Reservoir Dogs'?

4. The main court at the US Open Tennis Championship is named after which player?

5. Which character made his film debut in 1933 and starred in remakes in 1976 and 2005?

6. Whom did John Bercow succeed as Speaker of the House of Commons?

7. Reaching number eight in the charts in 1983, 'Rockit' was the only UK top ten hit for which artist?

8. Which director's films include 'This Is Spinal Tap' and 'The Princess Bride'?

9. Who played uber-villain 'Le Chiffre' in the 2006 James Bond film 'Casino Royale'?

10. 'The Galveston Giant' was the nickname of which ground-breaking heavyweight boxer?

11. Who won the Oscar for Best Actress in 1997 for her performance in 'As Good As It Gets'?

12. 'Bluebeard's Castle' was the only opera written by which Hungarian pianist and composer?

13. Which German director's films include 'Wings of Desire' and 'Buena Vista Social Club'?

Answers – page 361

14. Will Smith played Captain James West in which 1999 film?

15. Who was the first winner of the BBC Sports Personality of the Year award?

16. The 1986 single 'What Have You Done for Me Lately' was the first top five hit for which female singer?

17. What was the name of the character played by Rex Harrison in the film version of the musical 'My Fair Lady'?

18. Which fast-throwing dart player is known as 'The Dutch Destroyer'?

19. Which actor starred in the film 'Stand By Me', played Wesley Crusher in 'Star Trek: The Next Generation' and makes regular cameo appearances in 'The Big Bang Theory'?

20. Which Scottish engineer designed the Menai Bridge?

## Answers to Quiz 176: Pot Luck

1. Sisyphus
2. Ethiopia
3. John Donne
4. Arabic
5. James Caan
6. Julian Clary
7. Faisalabad
8. Muse
9. Thabo Mbeki
10. John Nash
11. Tess of the d'Urbervilles
12. Birmingham
13. Vladimir Nabokov
14. Cardinal John Henry Newman
15. Vaclav Havel
16. Guy Ritchie
17. William Burroughs
18. Coco Chanel
19. Scarborough
20. Dawn French

DIFFICULT

# Quiz 178: Pot Luck

1. The island of Trinidad lies just seven miles from the coast of which South American country?

2. Composer Ludwig van Beethoven was born in which German city?

3. What nationality was the playwright and poet Henrik Ibsen?

4. 'Delta Machine' was a 2013 album by which veteran synth-pop band?

5. David Ivor Davies is the real name of which Welsh actor and composer, after whom a famous award is named?

6. In 1964, Tanganyika joined with Zanzibar and Pemba Island to form which country?

7. In 2008, Kamalesh Sharma became the secretary-general of which organization?

8. Niccolo Paganini was a virtuoso on which musical instrument?

9. What was the first name of the composer Offenbach, who is best known for the light opera 'The Tales of Hoffmann'?

10. Cricketer Brian Lara was born on which Caribbean island?

11. 'Juno and the Paycock', 'The Silver Tassie', and 'Oak Leaves and Lavender' are works by which Irish playwright who died in 1964?

12. 'Inferno' is a 2013 novel by which best-selling author?

13. Who succeeded Charles de Gaulle as president of France in 1969?

14. What do the initials JB stand for in the name JB Priestley?

15. Which former world darts champion is nicknamed 'The Bronzed Adonis'?

Answers – page 363

16. Which Austrian philosopher's works included 'The Open Society and Its Enemies' and 'Objective Knowledge'?

17. Which Russian composer wrote the operas 'The Love for Three Oranges', 'The Betrothal in a Monastery' and 'War and Peace'?

18. Honiara is the capital city of which Commonwealth nation?

19. Who is the lead singer with Welsh rock band the Stereophonics?
    a) Kelly Jones
    b) Emlyn Middleton
    c) Gruff Rhys

20. Which Russian author learnt to ride a bike at the age of 67?
    a) Dostoevsky
    b) Solzhenitsyn
    c) Tolstoy

## Answers to Quiz 177: Alliterative Answers part 2

| | | | |
|---|---|---|---|
| 1. | Steve Staunton | 11. | Helen Hunt |
| 2. | David Davis | 12. | Béla Bartók |
| 3. | Michael Madsen | 13. | Wim Wenders |
| 4. | Arthur Ashe | 14. | Wild Wild West |
| 5. | King Kong | 15. | Christopher Chataway |
| 6. | Michael Martin | 16. | Janet Jackson |
| 7. | Herbie Hancock | 17. | Henry Higgins |
| 8. | Rob Reiner | 18. | Vincent van der Voort |
| 9. | Mads Mikkelsen | 19. | Wil Wheaton |
| 10. | Jack Johnson | 20. | Thomas Telford |

DIFFICULT

# Quiz 179: Sport part 2

1. Which manager steered Liverpool to European Cup victory in 1984?

2. In which year did Sir Roger Bannister become the the first man to run a mile in under 4 minutes?

3. Who was the only Italian in Europe's 2012 Ryder Cup-winning team?

4. Who was the first cricketer to score a double century in a One Day International?

5. Who in 2013 became the first Australian to win golf's US Masters?

6. Which was the only country to compete in all 26 sports at the 2012 London Olympics?

7. Which two London clubs were knocked out of the 2012/13 FA Cup at the semi-final stage?

8. How many players make up a water polo team?

9. The Lions, Tigers, Pistons, and Red Wings are professional sports teams based in which American city?

10. Who was the last team to win the old European Cup before it became the Champions League?

11. At which venue was that last final held?

12. Who was the first cricketer to captain his country in over 100 Test matches?

13. Kings Lynn Aces, Eastbourne Eagles, and Birmingham Brummies compete in which sport?

14. Jody Scheckter is the only Formula One driver from which country to have won the World Championship?

15. Who beat Tony O'Shea 7–1 in the final to win the 2013 BDO World Darts Championship?

16. Which country's Formula One Grand Prix is held at the Buddh International Circuit?

17. Which cricketer, who shares part of his name with a 19th-century British prime minister, took the catch that won England the Ashes in 1986/87?

18. How old was golfer Tianlang Guan when he made his debut at the US Masters in 2013?

19. How many times did Manchester United win the FA Cup with Sir Alex Ferguson as manager?
    a) four times  b) five times  c) six times

20. Who captained England in the most Test matches?
    a) Michael Atherton  b) Andrew Strauss
    c) Michael Vaughan

## Answers to Quiz 178: Pot Luck

| | | | |
|---|---|---|---|
| 1. | Venezuela | 11. | Sean O'Casey |
| 2. | Bonn | 12. | Dan Brown |
| 3. | Norwegian | 13. | Georges Pompidou |
| 4. | Depeche Mode | 14. | John Boynton |
| 5. | Ivor Novello | 15. | Steve Beaton |
| 6. | Tanzania | 16. | Karl Popper |
| 7. | The Commonwealth | 17. | Sergey Prokofiev |
| 8. | Violin | 18. | Solomon Islands |
| 9. | Jacques | 19. | Kelly Jones |
| 10. | Trinidad | 20. | Tolstoy |

DIFFICULT

# Quiz 180: Pot Luck

1. Which English designer created the 'petal' design for the 2012 Olympic cauldron as well as the new version of the classic Routemaster bus?

2. Who is older – Halle Berry or Julia Roberts?

3. The video game series 'Splinter Cell' is based on novels by which author?

4. The Daredevils are a T20 cricket team based in which Indian city?

5. 'Music of the Sun' was the 2005 debut album from which Barbadian singer?

6. Which former Israeli prime minister was assassinated by Yigal Amir in 1995?

7. Which comedian and actor said that he plans to give up his career as a funnyman in order to stand for the position of Mayor of London in 2020?

8. Which controversial Russian-born American novelist who died in 1982 was a proponent of the philosophy of Objectivism?

9. Which of the following actors is the eldest – Pierce Brosnan, John Travolta, or Denzel Washington?

10. Kananga and his tarot-reading mistress Solitaire were baddies in which James Bond film?

11. Which English colonial administrator founded the port city of Singapore and also co-founded London Zoo?

12. 'One Day I'm Going to Soar' was a 2012 album from which veteran British band?

13. Blonde Snapper won what title at Wimbledon on 26 May 2012?

14. What was the Rolling Stones' first UK number one hit single?

15. Which German-born author, who died in 2013, was the only writer to win both an Oscar and the Booker Prize (for 'Heat and Dust')?

16. Which US politician wrote the 2003 memoir 'Living History'?

17. Between 1955 and 1984, poet Philip Larkin was a librarian at which British university?

18. Which Canadian-born director's films include 'Cosmopolis', 'A Dangerous Method', and 'A History of Violence'?

19. Which Scottish actor was nominated for an Olivier Award in 2013 for his performance in Macbeth?
    a) Ewan McGregor
    b) James McAvoy
    c) Robert Carlyle

20. Brothers Ron and Russell Mael are members of which band?
    a) Depeche Mode
    b) Kraftwerk
    c) Sparks

## Answers to Quiz 179: Sport part 2

1. Joe Fagan
2. 1954
3. Francesco Molinari
4. Sachin Tendulkar
5. Adam Scott
6. Great Britain
7. Chelsea and Millwall
8. Seven
9. Detroit
10. Barcelona
11. Wembley
12. Graeme Smith
13. Speedway
14. South Africa
15. Scott Waites
16. India
17. Gladstone Small
18. 14
19. Five times
20. Michael Atherton

DIFFICULT

# Quiz 181: Old and New

1. What was the title of the 2009 UK number one album from US rockers Paramore?

2. What is the capital city of the US state of New Hampshire?

3. Which Merseyside club was a member of the Football League from 1923 until 1951?

4. Which children's card game is known in German as 'schwarzer Peter' and in France as 'vieux garçon'?

5. New Plymouth is a port city in which country?

6. 'The Staggers' is the nickname of which weekly magazine?

7. The 2002 album 'A New Day at Midnight' topped the charts for which British singer-songwriter?

8. Fredericton is the capital city of which Canadian province?

9. 'You Got It (The Right Stuff)' was a UK number one hit for which band?

10. 'The Kumuls' is the nickname of the rugby league team from which country?

11. Which magazine was created by Harold W Ross and published for the first time on 21 February 1925?

12. What is the smallest state in the American region known as New England?

13. Which actress won a Best Supporting Actress Bafta Award in 2006 for her performance in 'Crash'?

14. Who is the actor brother of 'EastEnders' star Laila Morse?

15. The Lockinge Stakes is a horse race run at which English racecourse?

16. Which American singer-songwriter and composer wrote the scores to the films 'Toy Story', 'Monsters, Inc.', and 'Cars'?

17. What is the name of the 2005 film starring Billy Bob Thornton as a little-league baseball coach trying to turn his team of misfits into champs?

18. 'Old New Borrowed and Blue' was a number one album in 1974 for which glam rockers?

19. 'Old Red Eyes Is Back' was a UK hit single in 1992 for which band?
    a) The Beautiful South
    b) Dexys Midnight Runners
    c) Divine Comedy

20. Chris Old was an England international at which sport?
    a) cricket
    b) rugby union
    c) squash

## Answers to Quiz 180: Pot Luck

1. Thomas Heatherwick
2. Halle Berry
3. Tom Clancy
4. Delhi
5. Rihanna
6. Yitzhak Rabin
7. Eddie Izzard
8. Ayn Rand
9. Pierce Brosnan
10. Live and Let Die
11. Sir Stamford Raffles
12. Dexys Midnight Runners
13. Greyhound Derby
14. It's All Over Now
15. Ruth Prawer Jhabvala
16. Hillary Clinton
17. Hull University
18. David Cronenberg
19. James McAvoy
20. Sparks

DIFFICULT

# Quiz 182: Pot Luck

1. Which character did Jeffrey Wright play in the James Bond films 'Casino Royale' and 'Quantum of Solace'?

2. 'Peter Grimes' and 'Billy Budd' are operas by which composer?

3. Agnes Gonxha Bojaxhiu was the birth name of which noted humanitarian?

4. 'Do It Like a Dude' was the 2010 debut single from which British singer?

5. Which Australian opera singer was known as 'La Stupenda'?

6. Which actress, who played Myrtle in the 2013 film version of 'The Great Gatsby', is married to comedian and actor Sacha Baron Cohen?

7. Who was the first batsman to score 15,000 runs in Test match cricket?

8. Which politician said, 'I am extraordinarily patient, provided I get my own way in the end'?

9. What was Charles Dickens' first novel?

10. A painting called 'La Rêve', which sold for $155m in 2013, was by which artist?

11. Which American writer's autobiography was published in 2010, 100 years after his death?

12. JRR Tolkien was a professor of English at which British university?

13. 'Comedown Machine' was a 2013 album by which American indie rockers?

14. Which Australian comedian played Judas in the 2013 revival of 'Jesus Christ Superstar'?

15. Jacopo Robusti was the real name of which Venetian painter whose 'Origin of the Milky Way' is hung in the National Gallery?

16. Who is older – Justin Bieber or One Direction's Harry Styles?

17. Which poet won a Pulitzer Prize in 1948 for 'The Age of Anxiety'?

18. What was the name of the family in the TV sitcom 'Desmond's'?

19. The 1980 novel 'Metroland' was the debut novel from which British author?
    a) Martin Amis
    b) Julian Barnes
    c) Ian McEwan

20. In 2013, David Miliband gave up his British political career to take up a role with which charity?
    a) International Rescue Committee
    b) Oxfam
    c) Save the Children

## Answers to Quiz 181: Old and New

1. Brand New Eyes
2. Concord
3. New Brighton
4. Old Maid
5. New Zealand
6. New Statesman
7. David Gray
8. New Brunswick
9. New Kids on the Block
10. Papua New Guinea
11. The New Yorker
12. Rhode Island
13. Thandie Newton
14. Gary Oldman
15. Newbury
16. Randy Newman
17. The Bad News Bears
18. Slade
19. The Beautiful South
20. Cricket

**DIFFICULT**

# Quiz 183: Connections

1. In the TV comedy Porridge, what was the name of the governor of Slade Prison?

2. Which Scottish historian wrote the books 'Empire: How Britain Made the Modern World', 'The Ascent of Money', and 'Civilization: The West and the Rest'?

3. Which former president of Liberia was found guilty of bearing responsibility for war crimes at a trial at the International Criminal Court in 2011?

4. Jessica Hynes played Cheryl Carroll and Sheridan Smith played Emma Kavanagh in which popular BBC comedy?

5. Golightly is the middle name of which actor whose TV credits include 'Casualty', 'Soldier, Soldier', and 'Waterloo Road'?

6. Who is the only Spaniard to have won the ladies' singles title at Wimbledon?

7. Which American musician, writer, and producer was the guitar player with disco giants Chic?

8. What is the second largest town on the Isle of Man?

9. Which French author wrote the 1885 novel 'Germinal'?

10. Which word, which means stone in German, is also used in English to describe an ornamental beer mug made from stoneware?

11. Named after a Scottish town, what type of textile pattern is characterized by colourful, curved abstract figures?

12. Who is the lead vocalist with heavy metal band Iron Maiden?

13. What is the name of the female-only prison in the London borough of Islington?

14. Which musician was the subject of the film 'Nowhere Boy'?

15. What is the English name for the high cylindrical military hat originally worn by Hungarian hussars?

16. Which American golfer won the US PGA on his major tournament debut in 2011?

17. Which British actor won an Emmy Award in 2009 for his portrayal of Benjamin Franklin in the miniseries 'John Adams'?

18. Which character from the TV sketch comedy 'The Fast Show', a parody of a music hall performer, had the catchphrase 'Where's me washboard'?
    a) Arthur Atkinson  b) Billy Bleach  c) Tommy Cockles

19. Who holds the record for the most men's singles titles at tennis' French Open?
    a) Bjorn Borg  b) Rafa Nadal  c) Pete Sampras

20. What is the connection between the answers above?

## Answers to Quiz 182: Pot Luck

1. Felix Leiter
2. Benjamin Britten
3. Mother Teresa of Calcutta
4. Jessie J
5. Dame Joan Sutherland
6. Isla Fisher
7. Sachin Tendulkar
8. Margaret Thatcher
9. The Pickwick Papers
10. Pablo Picasso
11. Mark Twain
12. Oxford
13. The Strokes
14. Tim Minchin
15. Tintoretto
16. Harry Styles
17. WH Auden
18. Ambrose
19. Julian Barnes
20. International Rescue Committee

DIFFICULT

# Quiz 184: Pot Luck

1. Zach, Larry, Don Kerr, Maggie Winslow, and Mike Costa are characters in which stage musical?

2. The winner of the Bollinger Everyman Wodehouse Prize for comic fiction has what type of animal named in their honour?

3. In 2008, which English author's chair and writing desk were sold at auction for £433,250?

4. Which doodling-inspired smartphone app was turned into a Channel 4 TV show in 2013?

5. The Rowley Mile Course is a feature of which English racecourse?

6. In 2011, John Cridland was appointed the Director-General of which business organization?

7. Krung Thep is the local name for which Asian capital city?

8. The Bridge of No Return links which two Asian countries?

9. Mark Loram was the last British world champion in which sport?

10. Which letter comes between iota and lambda in the Greek alphabet?

11. Which vegetable is the central ingredient in the Dutch soup 'Ertwensoep'?

12. If all 50 of the US state capitals were listed alphabetically, which city would be first on the list?

13. And what city would be last?

14. In Scrabble, which two tiles are worth 8 points?

15. Which flower provides the nickname of the South African cricket team?

16. Whom did Michael Bloomberg succeed as the Mayor of New York?

17. Found in the mountains of Europe, Asia, and north-eastern Africa, what type of animal is an ibex?

18. 'Kirimon' and 'Kikumon' are the imperial crests of which country?

19. 'Le coude' is the French word for part of the human body?
    a) elbow
    b) knee
    c) shin

20. Up to the end of 2012, how many parliamentary seats have been controlled by the same party since the reign of Queen Victoria?
    a) 22
    b) 32
    c) 42

## Answers to Quiz 183: Connections

1. Mr Venables
2. Niall Ferguson
3. Charles Taylor
4. The Royle Family
5. Robson Green
6. Conchita Martinez
7. Nile Rodgers
8. Ramsey
9. Emile Zola
10. Stein
11. Paisley
12. Bruce Dickinson
13. Holloway
14. John Lennon
15. Busby
16. Keegan Bradley
17. Tom Wilkinson
18. Arthur Atkinson
19. Rafa Nadal
20. They all mention part of the name of a successful football manager

DIFFICULT

# Quiz 185: Olympic Games

1. Which French resort hosted the 1992 Winter Olympics?

2. Which was the first American city to host the Summer Olympics?

3. Carl Hester, Laura Bechtolsheimer, and Charlotte Dujardin won gold for Britain at London 2012 in which event?

4. Eight players from which sport were disqualified from the 2012 games for trying to lose on purpose?

5. What is the penultimate event of an Olympic decathlon?

6. Which broadcaster was the inspiration for Mo Farah's 'Mobot' celebration?

7. Which Australian multiple Olympic gold medallist was part of the BBC's swimming commentary team at the 2012 games?

8. Katherine Copeland and Sophie Hosking won Olympic gold in 2012 in which sport?

9. Which company has sponsored every Olympic Games since 1928?

10. Which modern-day politician represented Great Britain in the 200m and the 4x100m relay at the 1964 Olympics?

11. Which British gold medallist said that he would be celebrating his success at the London games by 'watching the Olympics on TV with a beer and a bowl of crisps'?

12. Which American city hosted the 2002 Winter Olympics?

13. A total of 31 world records were set at the 2012 games, most of them in which sport?

14. Hasely Crawford, the first man from the Caribbean to win the men's 100m sprint gold, represented which country?

DIFFICULT

15. The 2018 Winter Olympics will be held in which country?

16. Who said after winning gold in 2012, 'There is almost slight melancholy. I realized on the podium that that's probably it for me. I don't think anything is going to top that'?

17. Which multiple gold medal winner carried the British flag at the closing ceremony of the 2012 games?

18. 47-year-old Josefa Idem competed at her eighth Olympics in 2012. In which sport?

19. Which country won the men's football gold at the 2012 games?
a) Brazil  b) Mexico  c) Netherlands

20. Which British former world boxing champion was working with the Angolan boxing team at the 2012 Olympics?
a) Nigel Benn  b) Chris Eubank  c) Richie Woodhall

## Answers to Quiz 184: Pot Luck

1. A Chorus Line
2. Pig
3. Charles Dickens
4. Draw Something
5. Newmarket
6. The CBI
7. Bangkok
8. North and South Korea
9. Speedway
10. Kappa
11. Pea
12. Albany (New York)
13. Trenton (New Jersey)
14. X and J
15. Protea
16. Rudy Giuliani
17. Goat
18. Japan
19. Elbow
20. 32

**DIFFICULT**

# Quiz 186: Pot Luck

1. Britt Ekland played 007's assistant Mary Goodnight in which James Bond film?

2. Which country rejoined NATO in 2009 following a self-imposed 43-year exile?

3. How many compartments are there on a standard European roulette wheel?

4. What was Elvis Presley's first UK number one single?

5. Which author created the fictional characters Alec Leamas, Toby Esterhase, and Percy Alleline?

6. Which waterway was built by French engineer Ferdinand de Lesseps and opened in 1869?

7. 'Indocilis privata loqui' (Not apt to disclose secrets) is the motto of which mysterious British organization?

8. Which layer of the earth's atmosphere lies between the tropopause and the stratopause?

9. Which popular puzzle game was created by American architect Howard Garns in 1979?

10. What was the most played song on British radio in 2012?

11. Which London satellite town, 34km north of the capital, was founded by Sir Ebenezer Howard in 1920?

12. Which of horse racing's five 'classic' races takes place earliest in the year?

13. Which Russian composer, who died in 1975, was nominated for an Ivor Novello Award in 2013 after a part of his 7th Symphony was incorporated into a song by Plan B?

14. 'Summerfolk', 'Children of the Sun', and 'Counterfeit Money' are works by which Russian playwright who died in 1936?

15. Which international business magnate filed for divorce from Wendi Deng in June 2013?

16. In Scrabble, what are the only two tiles that are worth 2 points?

17. Negus was the name given to the kings of which African country?

18. Which rescue organization was founded by Sir William Hillary on 4 March 1824?

19. In which branch of the arts is Ron Mueck a notable name?
    a) classical music
    b) dance
    c) sculpture

20. In which field is the James Tait Black Memorial Prize awarded?
    a) art
    b) literature
    c) physics

## Answers to Quiz 185: Olympic Games

| | | | |
|---|---|---|---|
| 1. | Albertville | 11. | Sir Chris Hoy |
| 2. | St Louis | 12. | Salt Lake City |
| 3. | Dressage | 13. | Swimming |
| 4. | Badminton | 14. | Trinidad and Tobago |
| 5. | Javelin | 15. | South Korea |
| 6. | Clare Balding | 16. | Bradley Wiggins |
| 7. | Ian Thorpe | 17. | Ben Ainslie |
| 8. | Rowing | 18. | Canoeing |
| 9. | Coca Cola | 19. | Mexico |
| 10. | Sir Menzies Campbell | 20. | Chris Eubank |

DIFFICULT

# Quiz 187: Politics part 2

1. In 2012, Portia Simpson-Miller became the prime minister of which Commonwealth country?

2. The UMP is a major political movement in which European country?

3. Which two countries were involved in a split known as the 'velvet divorce'?

4. In 2007, Donald Tusk was elected prime minister of which country?

5. Who was the first prime minister of Israel?

6. In 1944, Lebanon gained independence from which country?

7. In 2004, Alexander Lukashenko became the president of which Eastern European country?

8. The Five Star Grouping, Left Ecology Freedom, and The People of Freedom are political movements in which country?

9. The PSOE and PP are the main political parties in which European country?

10. Which 19th-century French politician and historian wrote 'Democracy in America'?

11. Which electoral system has the initials STV?

12. Which three politicians held the post of Foreign Secretary while Tony Blair was prime minister?

13. Which politician was the editor of 'The Spectator' magazine from 1999 to 2005?

14. Which politician wrote the book 'Back from the Brink: 1000 Days at Number 11'?

15. Which pair of Northern Irish politicians shared the Nobel Peace Prize in 1998?

Answers – page 381

16. In 2011, Elio Di Rupo was elected prime minister of which country?

17. Which veteran MP is nicknamed 'The Beast of Bolsover'?

18. Ladywood, Selly Oak, and Yardley are paliamentary constituencies in which English city?

19. Which former leader of the Conservative Party wrote an award-winning biography of William Pitt The Younger?
    a) Iain Duncan Smith
    b) William Hague
    c) Michael Howard

20. Who was the British prime minister at the start of the First World War?
    a) Herbert Asquith
    b) Stanley Baldwin
    c) Andrew Bonar Law

## Answers to Quiz 186: Pot Luck

1. The Man with the Golden Gun
2. France
3. 37
4. All Shook Up
5. John le Carré
6. The Suez Canal
7. The Magic Circle
8. Stratosphere
9. Sudoku
10. Domino by Jessie J
11. Welwyn Garden City
12. 2,000 Guineas
13. Dmitri Shostakovich
14. Maxim Gorky
15. Rupert Murdoch
16. D and G
17. Ethiopia
18. The Royal National Lifeboat Institution (RNLI)
19. Sculpture
20. Literature

DIFFICULT

# Quiz 188: Pot Luck

1. What was the Rolling Stones' last UK number one hit single?

2. Complete the title of the 2013 film starring Ryan Gosling: 'The Place Beyond the ...'

3. The 150th edition of which famous sporting annual was published in April 2013?

4. 'Last night I dreamt I went to Manderley again' is the opening line to which 1938 novel?

5. What was the first name of the 19th-century composer Mussorgsky?

6. Which Oscar-winning actress played nurse Megan Roach in the BBC medical drama 'Casualty'?

7. Which province of Canada is home to the largest population?

8. According to the Sunday Times Rich List 2013, who is the richest musician under the age of 30?

9. 'La Haye' is the French name for which European city?

10. In which month does the Cowes Week sailing regatta traditionally take place?

11. American model Patti Hansen is married to which member of the Rolling Stones?

12. What is the most commonly used noun in the English language?

13. 'The Modern Prometheus' is the subtitle to which classic horror novel?

14. 'I think it would be fun to run a newspaper' is a quote from which classic 1941 film?

15. Which American city is home to professional sports teams called the Browns, Cavaliers, and Indians?

16. Which European football team plays its home matches at the Westfalenstadion?

17. The corporate HQ of online giant Amazon.com is in which American city?

18. Actors Kiefer Sutherland, Boris Karloff, and Mischa Barton were all born in which city?

19. Who was the first player to score two maximum 147 breaks at snooker's World Championship?
a) Steve Davis  b) Stephen Hendry  c) Ronnie O'Sullivan

20. In 2013, Tom Stoppard wrote a special radio play to mark the anniversary of the release of which classic album?
a) Aladdin Sane  b) The Dark Side of the Moon
c) Innervisions

## Answers to Quiz 187: Politics part 2

1. Jamaica
2. France
3. Czech Republic and Slovakia
4. Poland
5. David Ben-Gurion
6. France
7. Belarus
8. Italy
9. Spain
10. Alexis de Tocqueville
11. Single transferable vote
12. Robin Cook, Jack Straw, and Margaret Beckett
13. Boris Johnson
14. Alistair Darling
15. John Hume and David Trimble
16. Belgium
17. Dennis Skinner
18. Birmingham
19. William Hague
20. Herbert Asquith

DIFFICULT

# Quiz 189: History part 2

1. Who was the British prime minister from 19 October 1963 until 16 October 1964?

2. The 1842 Treaty of Nanking ended which war?

3. The Peacock Throne was a symbol of the monarchy of which country?

4. The name of which 1970s TV detective was also a name given to troopers in Oliver Cromwell's Parliamentary cavalry?

5. The Battle of Dettingen in 1743 was part of which conflict?

6. What relation was Queen Victoria to King George III?

7. Which flower gave its name to a 2005 revolution in the former Soviet republic of Kyrgyzstan?

8. Who were the four British prime ministers during the reign of King George VI?

9. How old was Queen Victoria when she acceded to the throne?

10. Who was the British prime minister during the General Strike?

11. Habib Bourguiba was the president of which country from 1957 until 1987?

12. The Battle of Crécy was the first major engagement in which war?

13. Who was the last Roman Catholic king of England?

14. Millard Fillmore was the last president of the USA to represent which political party?

15. What was the name of the Cuban dictator overthrown by revolutionary forces led by Fidel Castro in 1959?

Answers – page 385

16. Who was the president of Russia between 2008 and 2012?

17. Who was the last English monarch to accompany his army into battle?

18. Who was the only US president to have served two terms in office with another president sitting in between?

19. At its end, the former Soviet Union was made up of how many republics?
    a) 12
    b) 15
    c) 18

20. The last battle of the English Civil War took place in which city?
    a) Leicester
    b) Nottingham
    c) Worcester

## Answers to Quiz 188: Pot Luck

1. Honky Tonk Women
2. Pines
3. Wisden Cricketers' Almanack
4. 'Rebecca' by Daphne Du Maurier
5. Modest
6. Brenda Fricker
7. Ontario
8. Adele
9. The Hague
10. August
11. Keith Richards
12. Time
13. Frankenstein
14. Citizen Kane
15. Cleveland
16. Borussia Dortmund
17. Seattle
18. London
19. Ronnie O'Sullivan
20. The Dark Side of the Moon

DIFFICULT

# Quiz 190: Pot Luck

1. Which European capital hosts the massive Sziget music festival?

2. The Janjaweed is a militia movement active in which country?

3. Kernewek is the native language of which part of the UK?

4. Raila Odinga is the former president of which African country?

5. Which journalist and broadcaster wrote the book 'In God We Doubt: Confessions of a Failed Atheist'?

6. What religious feast is celebrated on the fortieth day after Easter?

7. Ashley J 'Ash' Williams is the central character in which horror film trilogy?

8. The Hindu deity Ganesh is made up of which four creatures?

9. The 'Maglia Rosa' is awarded to the winner of which annual sporting event?

10. TV drama 'World Without End' is set during which conflict?

11. Garuda Airlines is the national flag carrier of which country?

12. Started in 312BC, which ancient Roman road stretched from Rome to Brindisi via Capua?

13. Which actor and singer played Napster founder Sean Parker in the 2010 film 'The Social Network'?

14. 'He was an old man who fished alone in a skiff in the Gulf Stream and he had gone eighty-four days now without taking a fish' is the opening line to which 1952 novel?

15. The flag of Bolivia is made up of which three colours?

Answers – page 387

16. Air Astana is the national flag carrier of which country?

17. Freddie Quell and Lancaster Dodd are the central characters in which Oscar-nominated 2012 film?

18. Which annual event was celebrated for the first time in Britain on 27 June 2009?

19. What would a person do with an amice?
    a) eat it
    b) smoke it
    c) wear it

20. In March 2013, an almost full-size replica of what was put up for sale on eBay?
    a) the House of Commons
    b) the Statue of Liberty
    c) the front of 10 Downing Street

## Answers to Quiz 189: History part 2

1. Sir Alec Douglas-Home
2. The Opium War
3. Iran
4. Ironside
5. The War of the Austrian Succession
6. Granddaughter
7. Tulip
8. Stanley Baldwin, Neville Chamberlain, Winston Churchill, and Clement Attlee
9. 18
10. Stanley Baldwin
11. Tunisia
12. The Hundred Years' War
13. James II
14. Whig Party
15. Fulgencio Batista
16. Dmitri Medvedev
17. George II
18. Grover Cleveland
19. 15
20. Worcester

DIFFICULT

# Quiz 191: Sport part 3

1. Who is Ireland's all-time leading rugby union international points scorer?

2. In Formula One, what colour flag warns a driver that he is about to be lapped and to let the faster car overtake?

3. Which English county cricket team plays its home games at Wantage Road?

4. In which month does the Royal Ascot race meeting traditionally take place?

5. Michael Campbell and Bob Charles are the only players from which country to win a golf major?

6. Who is the only player in the open era to win the men's singles at Wimbledon without dropping a set?

7. The football team CFR Cluj are based in which European country?

8. Which Grand Slam winner was appointed Andy Murray's coach in late 2011?

9. What title was won by Ryan Moore in 2008 and 2009, Paul Hanagan in 2010 and 2011, and Richard Hughes in 2012?

10. The Eclipse Stakes is run at which racecourse?

11. Which Australian did Roger Federer beat in 2003 to claim his first Wimbledon title?

12. Hashim Amla plays international cricket for which country?

13. The German football club Schalke 04 is based in which city?

14. Sixways Stadium is the home ground of which English Premiership rugby union team?

15. What nationality is the Formula One driver Daniel Ricciardo?

16. Which British fighter beat Aleksy Kuziemski in April 2011 to claim the WBO World Light Heavyweight title?

17. Which 100/1 outsider won the 2009 Grand National?

18. In which American city will you find a Major League Baseball team called the Athletics?

19. Which country won the Women's Cricket World Cup in 2013?
    a) Australia
    b) England
    c) New Zealand

20. Which Australian batsman, who retired from Test cricket in 2013, was known as 'Mr Cricket'?
    a) Michael Hussey
    b) Ricky Ponting
    c) Matthew Hayden

## Answers to Quiz 190: Pot Luck

1. Budapest
2. Sudan
3. Cornwall
4. Kenya
5. John Humphrys
6. Ascension Day
7. Evil Dead
8. Man, elephant, serpent, and mouse
9. The Giro d'Italia cycle race
10. The Hundred Years' War
11. Indonesia
12. Appian Way
13. Justin Timberlake
14. 'The Old Man and the Sea' by Ernest Hemingway
15. Red, yellow, and green
16. Kazakhstan
17. The Master
18. Armed Forces Day
19. Wear it
20. The House of Commons

**DIFFICULT**

# Quiz 192: Pot Luck

1. Which country has won football's Africa Cup of Nations the most times?

2. Which Oscar-nominated actor played Templeton 'Faceman' Peck in the 2010 film remake of 'The A Team'?

3. 'It's a funny thing about mothers and fathers. Even when their own child is the most disgusting little blister you could ever imagine, they still think that he or she is wonderful' are the opening words of which children's novel?

4. Ghostface was the name of the killer in which 1996 horror movie and its sequels in 1997, 2000, and 2004?

5. Who were the first winners of English football's League Cup?

6. What is a sternutation more commonly known as?

7. Plainmoor is the home ground of which English football club?

8. Mexico shares land borders with which three countries?

9. Which iconic Hollywood actress was born Betty Joan Perske?

10. Which film director was banned from the Cannes Film Festival in 2011 after making controversial comments about Hitler?

11. Erika Mitchell is the real name of which best-selling author?

12. Andre Young is the real name of which hip-hop star?

13. The award-winning play 'One Man, Two Guvnors' is set in which English city?

14. 'A man that doesn't spend time with his family can never be a real man' is a line from which classic 1972 film?

15. What colour jersey is worn by the leader of the Tour of Spain cycle race?

16. Which actor played Lucius Fox in the 'Batman: The Dark Knight' trilogy of films?

17. 'The Last Man in Europe' was a working title for which classic 1949 novel?

18. Which political leader was murdered in 1965 by Thomas Hagan?

19. Stichelton cheese is made in which English county?
    a) Dorset
    b) Lancashire
    c) Nottinghamshire

20. Complete the title of the award-winning 2011 film: 'Once Upon a Time in ...'
    a) Anatolia
    b) Romania
    c) Transylvania

## Answers to Quiz 191: Sports part 3

1. Ronan O'Gara
2. Blue
3. Northamptonshire
4. June
5. New Zealand
6. Bjorn Borg
7. Romania
8. Ivan Lendl
9. They were flat racing's Champion Jockey
10. Sandown
11. Mark Philippoussis
12. South Africa
13. Gelsenkirchen
14. Worcester Warriors
15. Australian
16. Nathan Cleverly
17. Mon Mome
18. Oakland
19. Australia
20. Michael Hussey

DIFFICULT

# Quiz 193: Myth and Legend

1. Which king of Mycenae, who was the brother of Menelaus, was murdered by Clytemnestra?

2. In Greek mythology, which King of Thebes unwittingly killed his father and subsequently married his mother?

3. Sometimes called Mulciber, who was the Roman god of fire?

4. By what collective name were Alecto, Megaera, and Tisiphone known?

5. What type of animal was Cerberus, the guard at the entrance of Hades?

6. In Norse mythology, Alfheim was the home of which supernatural beings?

7. Who designed the labyrinth at Knossos for King Minos of Crete?

8. Who was the twin sister of the Greek god Apollo?

9. Which mythical fire-breathing creature was part lion, part goat, and part serpent?

10. What was the name of the Roman goddess of the dawn whose Greek equivalent was Eos?

11. Zeus had which Greek god nailed to a mountain in the Caucasus and then sent an eagle to eat his immortal liver?

12. Cycnus, a mythical king of Liguria and lover of Phaeton, was turned into which bird?

13. Which huntress offered to marry anyone who could beat her in a race – but would spear anyone that she overtook?

14. In Greek mythology, what type of animal was Arion?

15. Which enchantress helped Jason obtain the Golden Fleece from her father before going on to marry him?

16. The name of which terrible Norse figures, whose number included Drynhild, Hok, and Herfjotur, means 'Choosers of the Slain'?

17. In Norse mythology, who was the personification of the air, the god of wisdom, and the spirit of the universe?

18. The Greek fertility god Pan had the horns, legs, and ears of which animal?

19. By what collective name were Stheno, Euryale, and Medusa known?
    a) Fates
    b) Muses
    c) Gorgons

20. In Norse mythology, Yggdrasil was what type of tree?
    a) ash
    b) elm
    c) oak

## Answers to Quiz 192: Pot Luck

1. Egypt
2. Bradley Cooper
3. 'Matilda' by Roald Dahl
4. Scream
5. Aston Villa
6. A sneeze
7. Torquay United
8. Belize, Guatemala, and the USA
9. Lauren Bacall
10. Lars Von Trier
11. EL James
12. Dr Dre
13. Brighton
14. The Godfather
15. Red
16. Morgan Freeman
17. Nineteen Eighty-Four
18. Malcolm X
19. Nottinghamshire
20. Anatolia

DIFFICULT

# Quiz 194: Pot Luck

1.  'The Death Instinct' and 'The Interpretation of Murder' are novels by which American author?

2.  Wanda Ventham, who played Cassandra's mum in 'Only Fools and Horses', is the real life mother of which famous actor?

3.  The M11 links London with which city?

4.  Which London borough is the most densely populated borough in the UK?

5.  Which best-selling singer also starred in the films 'Maid In Manhattan', 'Out of Sight', and 'Gigli'?

6.  The Royal Order of the Seraphim and the Order of the Polar Star are orders of chivalry in which European country?

7.  Paludian is a name sometimes used to describe a person from which Berkshire town?

8.  The ashes of which actor, who died in 1989, were later buried in Westminster Abbey?

9.  Hubert Cecil Booth was the inventor of which household appliance?

10. 'Decoded' is the title of the autobiography of which hip-hop star?

11. Ellis Bell was the pen name of which 19th-century English author?

12. What is the Australian equivalent of the UK telephone number 999?

13. 'Trimalchio in West Egg' was an alternative title of which 1925 novel?

14. Quinine is obtained from the bark of which tree?

Answers – page 395

15. Who was the first vice-president of the USA?

16. Which country hosts a massive music festival called Oxegen?

17. 'Ours is essentially a tragic age, so we refuse to take it tragically' is the opening line to which 1928 novel?

18. Which Norse god rode a horse called Sleipnir?

19. How old was William Gladstone when he retired as prime minister?
    a) 83
    b) 84
    c) 85

20. Who published an online archive of 130 watercolours in spring 2013?
    a) Tony Blair
    b) Bill Clinton
    c) Prince Charles

## Answers to Quiz 193: Myth and Legend

1. Agamemnon
2. Oedipus
3. Vulcan
4. The Furies
5. Dog
6. Elves
7. Daedalus
8. Artemis
9. Chimaera
10. Aurora
11. Prometheus
12. Swan
13. Atalanta
14. Horse
15. Medea
16. Valkyries
17. Odin
18. Goat
19. Gorgons
20. Ash

DIFFICULT

# Quiz 195: Movie Taglines

Identify the movies associated with the following taglines:

1. 'An adventure 65 million years in the making.' (1993)

2. 'Vietnam can kill me, but it can't make me care.' (1987)

3. 'A romantic comedy. With Zombies.' (2003)

4. 'We are not alone' (1977)

5. 'Her life was in their hands. Now her toe is in the mail.' (1998)

6. 'After a night they can't remember comes a day they'll never forget.' (2000)

7. 'First they took his daughter. Now they're coming for him.' (2012)

8. 'Love is in the hair.' (1998)

9. 'The movie was fake. The mission was real.' (2012)

10. 'Family isn't a word. It's a sentence.' (2001)

11. 'Good cops. Bad hair.' (2004)

12. 'One man's struggle to take it easy.' (1986)

13. 'To enter the mind of a killer she must challenge the mind of a madman.' (1991)

14. 'Five criminals. One line up. No coincidences.' (1995)

15. 'Collide with destiny.' (1997)

16. 'Before Sam was murdered, he told Molly he'd love and protect her forever.' (1990)

17. 'The search for our beginning could lead to our end.' (2012)

18. 'You won't know the facts until you've seen the fiction.' (1994)

19. 'Man has made his match ... now it's his problem.' (1982)

20. 'He's the only kid ever to get into trouble before he was born.' (1985)

## Answers to Quiz 194: Pot Luck

1. Jed Rubenfeld
2. Benedict Cumberbatch
3. Cambridge
4. Islington
5. Jennifer Lopez
6. Sweden
7. Slough
8. Sir Laurence Olivier
9. Vacuum cleaner
10. Jay Z
11. Emily Brontë
12. 000
13. The Great Gatsby
14. Cinchona tree
15. John Adams
16. Republic of Ireland
17. Lady Chatterley's Lover
18. Odin
19. 84
20. Prince Charles

DIFFICULT

# Quiz 196: Pot Luck

1. Who was US president Lyndon Johnson's vice-president?

2. Pierre Omidyar was the founder of which giant online company?

3. The genre of dance music known as techno originated in which American city?

4. 'Janner' is a nickname given to people from which English county?

5. What is the largest of London's eight royal parks?

6. Which breed of dog has won the Best in Show title at Crufts the most times?

7. Who was the first British footballer to be involved in a £2m transfer?

8. Which actress was named the world's 'Most Beautiful' in 2013 according to 'People' magazine?

9. The Colorado Party is a major political movement in which South American country?

10. Which controversial England rugby union international was hit by a bus while on a team pub crawl in April 2013?

11. Purple Day is a day aimed at raising awareness about which disease?

12. What Oxfordshire town gives its name to a flat currant-filled pastry, similar to an Eccles cake?

13. The famous Old Bushmills Distillery is located in which county of Northern Ireland?

14. Which British trade union has the initials USDAW?

15. What does the L in Samuel L Jackson stand for?

Answers – page 399

16. Brian Warner is the real name of which alliterative American alternative musician, born in Ohio in 1969?

17. After how many years is a sapphire anniversary celebrated?

18. James Wattana was the first player from which country to take part in the World Snooker Championship?

19. +91 is the international dialling code for which Commonwealth country?
    a) Canada
    b) India
    c) South Africa

20. Which museum was temporarily forced to close in April 2013 following a spate of pickpocket thefts?
    a) The Louvre
    b) MOMA
    c) Prado

## Answers to Quiz 195: Movie Taglines

1. Jurassic Park
2. Full Metal Jacket
3. Shaun of the Dead
4. Close Encounters of the Third Kind
5. The Big Lebowski
6. Dude, Where's My Car
7. Taken 2
8. There's Something About Mary
9. Argo
10. The Royal Tenenbaums
11. Starsky and Hutch
12. Ferris Bueller's Day Off
13. The Silence of the Lambs
14. The Usual Suspects
15. Titanic
16. Ghost
17. Prometheus
18. Pulp Fiction
19. Blade Runner
20. Back to the Future

**DIFFICULT**

# Quiz 197: Classical Music and Opera

1. Lang Lang is a world-renowned performer on which musical instrument?

2. 'Music for 18 Musicians', 'Clapping Music', and 'Different Trains' are works by which contemporary American minimalist composer?

3. Which composer wrote the three-act oratorio 'Theodora'?

4. Made up largely of Middle Eastern musicians, the West-Eastern Divan Orchestra is in fact based in which European city?

5. Which instrument is traditionally used to tune an orchestra?

6. Handel's 'Messiah' was first performed in which city?

7. Which of Beethoven's symphonies is known as the 'Pastoral Symphony'?

8. Which Italian composer said, 'Wagner has lovely moments but awful quarters of an hour'?

9. What nationality was the composer Zoltán Kodály?

10. Which composer wrote the incidental music to the Ibsen play 'Peer Gynt'?

11. Composers Giuseppe Verdi and Richard Wagner were both born in which year?

12. In which country was Percy Grainger born?

13. Which contemporary British composer wrote the soundtracks to films including 'Man on Wire', 'The Cook, The Thief, His Wife & Her Lover', and 'Gattaca'?

14. Pianist and conductor Daniel Barenboim was born in which city?

15. 'Turandot' was the last opera written by which composer?

16. 'Ariadne auf Naxos' is an opera written by which composer?

17. 'Il Prete Rosso' was the nickname of which composer?

18. Composers Edward Elgar, Gustav Holst, and Frederick Delius all died in which year?

19. 2013 marks the centenary of the birth of which British composer?
a) Benjamin Britten  b) Sir Harrison Birtwistle
c) Ralph Vaughan Williams

20. What is the nickname of Mozart's 41 symphony?
a) Mars Symphony  b) Jupiter Symphony
c) Saturn Symphony

## Answers to Quiz 196: Pot Luck

1. Hubert H Humphrey
2. eBay
3. Detroit
4. Devon
5. Richmond Park
6. Cocker spaniel
7. Mark Hughes
8. Gwyneth Paltrow
9. Paraguay
10. Danny Cipriani
11. Epilepsy
12. Banbury
13. Antrim
14. Union of Shop, Distributive, and Allied Workers
15. Leroy
16. Marilyn Manson
17. 45
18. Thailand
19. India
20. The Louvre

DIFFICULT

# Quiz 198: Pot Luck

1. Who directed the classic 1984 gangster film 'Once Upon a Time in America'?

2. 'Elysium' was a 2012 album by which veteran British band?

3. 'Nisi Dominus frustra' (It is vain without the Lord) is the motto of which British city?

4. What nationality is the professional snooker player Dechawat Poomjaeng?

5. +33 is the international dialling code for which European country?

6. What is the largest of New York's five boroughs by population?

7. The House of Wangchuck is the ruling dynasty of which Asian country?

8. What is the second largest city in Greece?

9. What is the name of the virtual currency developed in 2009 by an anonymous group of programmers using the pseudonym Satoshi Nakamoto?

10. 'Lady Writing a Letter with her Maid' is a famous painting by which Dutch master?

11. Which writer and comedian wrote the 2013 BBC comedy 'The Wright Way'?

12. Prior to Helen Mirren in 2007, who was the last Briton to win the Oscar for Best Actress?

13. What nationality was the playwright August Strindberg?

14. Which English architect designed the Bank of England building?

15. In which game was José Raúl Capablanca a world champion?

16. David James was the first goalkeeper to make 500 appearances in the Premier League. Who in April 2013 became the second to reach that milestone?

17. 'The Idiot', 'The Brothers Karamazov', and 'The Possessed' are novels by which Russian author?

18. Which actress and comedian married Mark Bignell in spring 2013?

19. Before becoming an actor, what was Harrison Ford's occupation?
    a) carpenter
    b) electrician
    c) plumber

20. In which branch of the arts is Lynn Chadwick a notable name?
    a) classical music
    b) dance
    c) sculpture

## Answers to Quiz 197: Classical Music and Opera

1. Piano
2. Steve Reich
3. Handel
4. Seville
5. Oboe
6. Dublin
7. Symphony No. 6
8. Rossini
9. Hungarian
10. Edvard Grieg
11. 1813
12. Australia
13. Michael Nyman
14. Buenos Aires
15. Puccini
16. Richard Strauss
17. Vivaldi
18. 1934
19. Benjamin Britten
20. Jupiter Symphony

DIFFICULT

# Quiz 199: Anagrams

Rearrange the letters to make the names of TV comedies:

1. So heads floor nylons

2. Either been newts

3. Oily feral thyme

4. China zen kit

5. Evil fry cohabited

6. A feeler shot twin mums

7. Revere a nosy budgie

8. Poked on dehydrated

9. Oust a babe soulfully

10. Dents teaspoon

11. Oft hitch kite

12. Daft three

13. Advancing yeast

14. Onion got gut

15. Peruse a pancake pigpen

16. Behind navy gamble

17. Ebullient hen hit

18. A bread rose fifth

19. Honours lapel

20. Eighty babe throng

## Answers to Quiz 198: Pot Luck

1. Sergio Leone
2. The Pet Shop Boys
3. Edinburgh
4. Thai
5. France
6. Brooklyn
7. Bhutan
8. Thessaloniki (Salonica)
9. Bitcoin
10. Vermeer
11. Ben Elton
12. Emma Thompson in 1992
13. Swedish
14. Sir John Soane
15. Chess
16. Mark Schwarzer
17. Fyodor Dostoevsky
18. Dawn French
19. Carpenter
20. Sculpture

**DIFFICULT**

# Quiz 200: Pot Luck

1. Jame 'Buffalo Bill' Gumb was a character in which 1991 film thriller?

2. Who played Superman's father in the 2013 film 'Man of Steel'?

3. Jason Todd Smith is the real name of which veteran American hip-hop star and actor?

4. Which British author, best known for his work with film directors Danny Boyle and Michael Winterbottom, also wrote the sequels to 'Chitty Chitty Bang Bang'?

5. Felix Ungar and Oscar Madison are the central characters in which classic 1968 film comedy?

6. Who was the first player to win the World Snooker Championship at the Crucible Theatre?

7. 'Mathematical Principles of Natural Philosophy' is a work by which physicist and mathematician?

8. Which is the only British football team to have beaten Barcelona home and away in a single European tie?

9. 'The Cunning Little Vixen' is an opera written by which Czech composer?

10. The Hugh Lane Gallery is located in which city?

11. The Kirkstall Lane End and the Football Ground End are features of which English Test cricket venue?

12. Stravinsky's 'Rite of Spring' was premiered in which European city?

13. In warfare, what do the initials IED stand for?

14. Johnny Depp played which bank-robber in the 2009 film 'Public Enemies'?

15. What is the female equivalent of golf's Ryder Cup?

16. In 'The Simpsons', what is the first name of police Chief Wiggum?

17. Up to 2012, who was the last player to win the men's singles at Wimbledon whose surname starts with a vowel?

18. The Broadfield Stadium is the home ground of which English football club?

19. Vaisakhi is a major festival in which religion?
    a) Buddhism
    b) Hinduism
    c) Sikhism

20. How old was Emily Brontë when she died?
    a) 20
    b) 30
    c) 40

## Answers to Quiz 199: Anagrams

1. Only Fools and Horses
2. The Inbetweeners
3. The Royle Family
4. Citizen Khan
5. The Vicar of Dibley
6. Last of the Summer Wine
7. Are You Being Served
8. Drop the Dead Donkey
9. Absolutely Fabulous
10. Steptoe and Son
11. The Thick of It
12. Father Ted
13. Gavin and Stacey
14. Not Going Out
15. Keeping Up Appearances
16. Men Behaving Badly
17. The Thin Blue Line
18. Birds of a Feather
19. Open All Hours
20. The Big Bang Theory

**DIFFICULT**

# Get quizzical with the full Collins quiz range

**NEW**

Available in paperback and ebook.

**NEW**

Available in paperback and ebook.

**NEW**

Available in paperback.

Available in paperback and ebook.

Available in paperback and ebook.

Available in paperback and ebook.

Available in paperback and ebook.

Available in paperback and ebook.

All **Collins** quiz range titles in paperback are RRP £6.99. Ebook prices may vary.

Find more information on our products at www.collinslanguage.com.
Available to buy from all good booksellers.

Follow us on Twitter  @collinsdict          Find Collins Dictionary on Facebook